World University Library

The World University Library is an international series
of books, each of which has been specially commissioned.
The authors are leading scientists and scholars from all over
the world who, in an age of increasing specialisation, see the
need for a broad, up-to-date presentation of their subject.
The aim is to provide authoritative introductory books for
university students which will be of interest also to the general
reader. The series is published in Britain, France, Germany,
Holland, Italy, Spain, Sweden and the United States.

Frontispiece. Aphids on a plant stem. Aphids are involved in most
of the problems of insect ecology: population studies;
re-colonisation; group-effects; damage to plants by direct attack
and by disease transmission; and problems of control.

Rémy Chauvin

The World of
an Insect

**Translated from the French
by Harold Oldroyd**

World University Library

**McGraw-Hill Book Company
New York   Toronto**

© Rémy Chauvin 1967
Translation © 1967 by George Weidenfeld and Nicolson Limited
Library of Congress Catalog Card Number 65–23823
Phototypeset by BAS Printers Limited, Wallop, Hampshire, England
Printed by Officine Grafiche Arnoldo Mondadori, Verona, Italy

Contents

Preface

My aim in this book is to explain quite a narrow aspect of ecology, and one that is peculiarly European; it is very little known in the rest of the world, especially in the USA. I make absolutely no claim to range over the wide expanse of ecological science, in many sections of which the British, for example, have established a reputation, and which have been described in many other places and by many other people.

It is only very recently that research workers, especially those of the German-speaking countries, have realised that by studying the cultivated field it is possible to reach a much greater precision than was previously possible. This is because we are dealing with a *uniform vegetational cover*. There has grown up a whole school devoted to this kind of work, which is bringing to light some very odd conclusions, not only about ecology, but about evolution in general. For example, the populating by insects of empty areas can be studied very conveniently, and with very great precision, when a new crop is cultivated in a place where it has never grown before.

The field of alfalfa (lucerne), to which so much prominence is given in this book, has no special importance in itself, but is chosen as a convenient example simply because it goes on flowering throughout a great part of the year. The study of the field of alfalfa has introduced techniques that are both new and important.

Introduction

When one takes up the study of insects it becomes obvious that, contrary to the general impression, nature does not seem to have expended all its energy on the vertebrate animals and on man. This idea has taken root because man seems to have been a biological success, both in quality and in numbers. Yet alongside him is milling the vast mass of the insects, making up four-fifths of all living beings. We must try to realise, although it is very nearly impossible to do so, that the number of described species of insects is certainly more than 600,000, and that every year two or three thousand new species are discovered. There are more species of flies in France than there are of mammals in the whole world.

The criticism that perhaps what is called a species among insects may be little more than a whim of the systematist, and that in reality insects differ only slightly among themselves, is unfounded; between species, or between genera of insects there are gaps which may be as great as that between a mouse and an elephant.

In one field of alfalfa (lucerne), according to Boness, there have been counted 790 species of insects, and nearly five hundred species in a cornfield. The 'biomass', as it is called, that is presented by the insects of a single acre of ground comes to quite an appreciable weight, without needing to use social insects as an example: in fact the honey-bee is not the only insect that can be bought by the pound at the present time. Moreover, every hive requires annually over 100 kilograms of nectar, and about 25 kilograms of pollen, collected grain by grain from the anthers of flowers. As for the ants, the figures are still more incredible. The red ants of our woodlands, which make those mounds of pine-needles, live in colonies each of which contains a very great number of individuals, sometimes two or three millions, built up by a large number of queens. A single nest of *Formica polyctena* has been known to have 5,000 sexually active queens.

Such colonies of ants are very active predators, and the Germans have calculated that one single colony may gather every day from 800 grams to one kilogram of food, made up of complete dead insects, and others that have been cut up into fragments. In the

Italian Alps counts have been made of more than a million nests of the red ant, comprising 300 million million individuals. Each year the ants are active for about 200 days, and they may destroy 15,000 tons of harmful insects.

These fantastic figures are nevertheless greatly exceeded in certain circumstances; when nature, run amok, creates a swarm of locusts. The gregarious grasshopper that is known in English as the Desert Locust (*Schistocerca gregaria*) is a big insect, weighing from two to three grams, which normally lives in very small numbers on the southern margin of the Sahara desert. When under the influence of climatic factors not yet entirely understood this insect starts to multiply, and gives rise to a crazy mass of locusts, this swarm may cover at one time one hundred square kilometres, and the weight of the insects concerned has been estimated at 70,000 tons.

When they descend upon a cultivated area there are often three or four locusts on every blade of cereal in the crop, and each gives two or three quick bites of its mandibles. That is enough to ensure that the field is completely stripped in little more than a quarter of an hour. It must be seen to be believed. At the time when Künckel

Left. A swarm of locusts (*Schistocerca gregaria*) descending on a valley in the region of Marrakesh. The locusts are seen as black specks against the sky, and look like large flakes of snow against the hills; some can be seen on the ground. *Below*. Here the individual locusts can be seen more distinctly against the sky, but the photograph does not give a true impression of the *density* of the swarm, which perceptibly cuts down the sunlight.

d'Herculais studied swarms of locusts in Algeria in 1880, the Arabs were being paid to dig up and collect together the egg-pods that the locusts laid in the soil. The pile soon reached to the first storey of the houses . . . !

Thus the insects, which everyone knows can be found anywhere, can also build up in one place a colossal mass of living matter. I said that they can be found anywhere. This is because their way of life, and their extreme resistance to adverse conditions, allow them to become adapted to every kind of environment. One environment that is colonised only with extreme reluctance is the ocean. No doubt truly marine insects do exist, but they are very few indeed. In contrast, insects colonise every other environment in vast numbers. Thus:

The *air*. Up to heights of about 1,500 to 2,000 metres insects form an aerial plankton comparable to the plankton of the sea, and on which many birds depend for their food. To appreciate the density of this plankton it is sufficient to consider the number of tiny insects that can be seen dancing in a shaft of sunlight.

Fresh water. The superficial layers are the most heavily colonised, because the method of respiration of insects obliges them to come more or less regularly to the surface to take atmospheric air. On the other hand they are not greatly dependent – much less so than are the fishes – upon the purity of the water in which they live. The water may be quite foul, and yet not deter mosquitoes and other flies from breeding in it.

Fresh water may also be frozen, in the form of ice or snow. One kind of Orthopteron, *Grylloblatta*, lives under such conditions, and is even dependent on them, because it soon dies if the temperature rises above freezing. In the very hot water of geysers (70–80°C) mosquito larvae develop very well, and are almost the only creatures except a few heat-loving bacteria that can withstand such high temperatures. Other liquids besides water sometimes support insect life. A notable example is petroleum, which is the chosen milieu of the fly *Psilopa petrolei*, which lives in seepage pools of crude oil, and feeds on the dead bodies of insects that fall in. Its intestine also contains symbiotic bacteria that can transform the petroleum into proteins that can be digested by the insect, so that those research workers who hope to extract edible materials from petroleum products have been anticipated by the insects.

The *dry land* is the great setting for insect populations. They penetrate into the ground, but only to quite a shallow depth, which does not exceed some tens of centimetres, the extent of the decomposing vegetable matter upon which the insects feed. But the most inhospitable zones have their insects, and the insect fauna of deserts is far from negligible. Most insects in these regions are nocturnal, because during the day the surface of the ground is heated to more than 80°C, and makes it nearly impossible for any living thing, especially if it is small, to move about actively. The insects therefore hide in holes, and only come out at night to chew vegetable fragments, which are moist with the dew that condenses during the night hours.

Ants and termites that live in the open desert take a more active part in digging themselves in. They excavate deep pits which may be more than 36 metres deep, as far down as the water-table (the permanent level of water in the soil). A continuous chain of workers

Figure 1. Cross-section of a single log, showing five microclimates for the wood-boring beetle *Ips typographicus*. Zone 1, most exposed to the sun, may reach a surface temperature of 50°C, and here the beetle does not lay its eggs. Zones 2 and 3 are still too warm; in zone 3 the eggs may hatch, but the larvae will die. Zone 5, in contrast, is too humid, and 75–92 % of the larvae will die. Only in zone 4 are both temperature and humidity favourable (after Geiger).

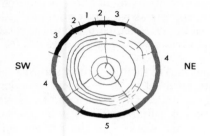

bears the precious liquid to the surface, in such abundance that in the middle of those arid surroundings a termite's nest in the desert is sometimes so humid that one can raise drops of water by scraping the surface with one's hand.

The arctic regions shelter, among others, those dreadful mosquitoes whose larvae are able to withstand without damage the prolonged frost of the winter. As soon as warmth returns they give rise to millions of vigorous adult mosquitoes, which make life in those parts more disagreeable than it is in tropical Africa.

These habitats are extraordinary enough, but nearer home, in our own fields and forests, insects thrive just the same. And here we must beware of deluding ourselves that they are living in 'our' fields, and 'our' forests! Because they are individually so small a new conception arises, and will dominate all that we have to say about their biology; the conception of a *microclimate*. This idea will be developed at leisure in the first chapter: but it must be understood at this point that we shall be dealing with a series of environments, superimposed one on another, and in which temperature, gain and loss of heat, and humidity are not on the scale that we are accustomed to, or which we can easily comprehend. Moreover, one insect may often be living in a microclimate quite different from that of another insect close by.

If we also allow for the differences in sensory equipment between insects and ourselves, we shall understand even more clearly that the insect that lives alongside us is really living in a totally different world. It does not see the same colours as we do, it does not hear the same sounds, it does not feel the same temperature in the same way, and most of all it reacts to certain stimuli that we do not feel, and still do not understand.

The immense variety of insects makes them favourite subjects for laboratory experiment. Whatever the line of research, genetics, behaviour, study of development under any given conditions, an insect can always be found that is suitable. There is a gigantic literature about insects, and twenty works like the present one would not cope with it. I shall therefore limit myself to *entomological ecology*, the science of insect populations in nature, in the woods, in pasture-land, and especially in cultivated land – that magnificent and culminating ecological experience, so little understood, and so unjustly neglected. Discussion of this special environment in relation to insects, and of their population dynamics there, will be the core of my subject.

1 The microclimate of an insect

Perhaps Science is no more than the laborious rediscovery of the obvious. The microclimate is a good example of this. Scientists began by inventing 'macroclimatology', which is so important for the health of man. Once the principles of measuring temperature, pressure and humidity had been discovered, the first step was to carry these out under controlled conditions. It was therefore decided to do these things in a special chamber, ventilated, but shaded, placed about two metres above a lawn: a Stevenson screen.

After which the medical climatologists decided that measurements taken in such a meteorological screen corresponded only very approximately with those found inside human dwellings. This was the cause of a mass of difficulties which are still only incompletely solved. After all, man does not spend his life out on the lawn, inside a meteorological screen, but mostly in his house, where he takes refuge whenever it is too hot or too cold. One physiologist has even remarked that quite half of a human life is spent at 30°C, because this is the temperature that usually exists under the bedclothes. But it is not our present purpose to study climate in relation to human health.

One scientist, the German Rudolf Geiger, pointed out that what is taking place at a height of six feet, inside a screen on a level with a man's face has little bearing on what is happening down by his feet, and even less on conditions among the tops of trees. His conclusion was that it was necessary to create a new branch of meteorology, *microclimatology*, which should concern itself with meteorological levels that are significant in botany and in entomology.

Problems of instrumentation

Geiger soon ran into great difficulties in finding suitable instruments, difficulties so great that he proposed to define microclimatology as beginning at 'the moment when the meteorologist changes his instruments'. This is not at once obvious to the non-specialist, so we must go into some detail.

Consider, for example, measurement of temperature. The micro-

Figure 2. Various ways in which the surface of the ground gains and loses heat *during the daytime*. Green arrows indicate heat gains, black arrows heat losses, the breadth of the arrows showing the relative intensity of each source of gain or loss (after Geiger).

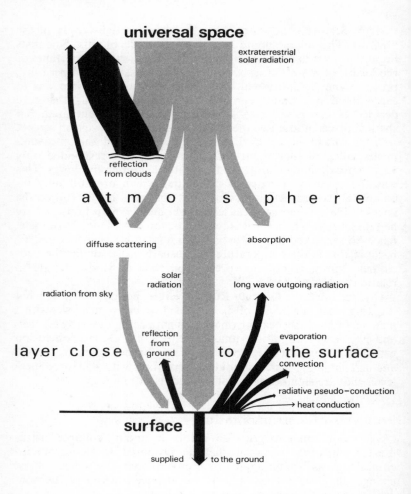

Figure 3. Various ways in which the surface
of the ground gains or loses heat *after dark*.
Green arrows indicate heat gains, black
arrows heat losses, the breadth of the arrows
showing the relative intensity of each source
of gain or loss (after Geiger).

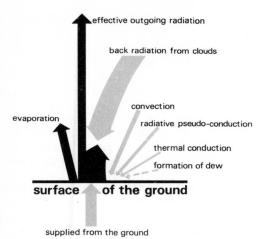

climatologist will give a hollow laugh if you suggest using a simple
thermometer. If you want to measure the temperature one centimetre above the soil, putting over it a standard screen of the type
already mentioned will completely alter the very conditions that you
are trying to record by absorbing heat from the sun, and radiating
some in return; moreover, as we shall see later, the microclimatic
temperature varies from one centimetre to another. It is essential,
therefore, to get rid of the screen. But then the thermometer will be
freely exposed to the rays of the sun, on the one hand, and to
radiation reflected back from the soil and the vegetation, on the
other. The thermometer reading will be meaningless. The space
under investigation can be protected by surrounding it with two
concentric cylinders of metal, lightly silvered, between which there
is a vacuum, so that when the metal warms up in the sun no heat
is radiated into the interior. After a few minutes the cylinder reaches
equilibrium with the surrounding air, and then the thermometer
measures the correct temperature.

Alongside the dry thermometer can be placed a second with its bulb wrapped in a wet cloth, thus providing a wet-and-dry bulb psychrometer. The drier the surrounding air, the more rapidly the moisture evaporates, thus cooling the wet bulb, which always reads a lower temperature than the dry bulb. Special tables are provided from which the temperature difference can be converted into a measure of relative humidity.

More refined methods can be used, such as the thermo-electric pile. The total solar radiation can be measured by such a pile in which the surface presented to the sun is blackened. For micro-measurements along the surface of a leaf, for example, thermo-electric needles can be used.

The measurement of temperatures and radiant heat may be simple in open locations, but becomes much more difficult in wooded areas. Everyone has seen the round spots of light that are produced on the ground by rays of sunlight which penetrate the leaves. How can the mean value of the radiation reaching a square metre of soil be assessed, except by a very large number of measurements? It is very complicated, and satisfactory techniques are still wanting.

The same problem is met with in relation to measurements of rainfall. Nothing would seem simpler than to put a rain-gauge, a sort of cylindrical receptacle, out on an open space and record the number of centimetres of rain that fall in it. Actually even this is not as simple as all that, because a German meteorologist had the idea of setting out, not one, but several scores of rain-gauges, several metres apart. He demonstrated in this way that their readings were not remotely comparable, and that rain has a very irregular distribution over the ground.

Under trees it is another matter again. We know, of course, that trees stop a certain proportion of the rain-drops, because we shelter under them in a downpour; but what proportion is stopped in this way? This may be of vital importance for those animals which normally live under the cover of the trees. Clarke built an ingenious yet very simple apparatus, which he called an 'inter-

Figure 4. During the middle of the day the relative humidity of the air decreases, and the water vapour pressure increases. The effect of height above the ground is opposite in the two cases; the change of relative humidity is greater at 100 cm than at 5 cm, but the change of water vapour pressure is greatest near the ground.

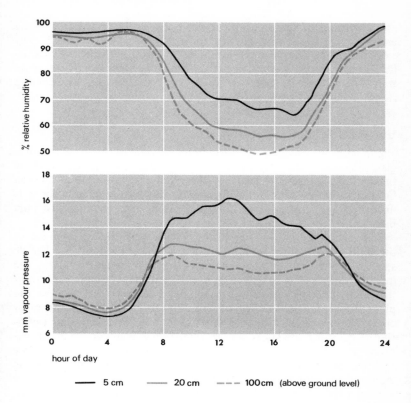

ceptometer'. Imagine a container with an area of one metre square, which is subdivided into sections ten centimetres wide. Five of such smaller containers are placed on the soil, of a wheatfield, for example, and the five others on top of the stems. Under these conditions the difference between the upper and the lower set of containers measures the power of interception of the vegetation. It is found to be considerable (we shall come back to this point), and the stems of such a crop can easily intercept up to 60 % of the water during slight or moderate rain.

Thus insects which move about on the soil surface in a wheat-field live, *as far as amount of precipitation is concerned*, in a climate that is drier than the open air in the same spot. As far as receiving radiation is concerned, it is also cooler.

Vegetation and microclimates

We must now consider, from the point of view of the bioclimatologist, the conditions provided by an isolated plant, and above all by particularly interesting parts of the plant, for example its leaves. Of the radiation that falls on a leaf, some is reflected, some is absorbed and causes a rise in temperature, and the smallest part passes through the leaf.

The proportion that is reflected varies with the wavelength of the light. In the ultra-violet almost all is absorbed; in the visible spectrum one fifth or at most a quarter is reflected; while in the infra-red most of it is reflected. Clearly all this controls the extent to which the leaf is warmed by the sun, all the more because the plant absorbs a great deal of the solar radiation, and the most energetic part of it. The transparency of the leaves to solar radiation is poor for the short waves. In the visible spectrum the transmission varies from 5 % to 20 %, with a maximum in the yellow and the green; but the greatest transmission takes place in the infra-red, of which, on the other hand, as we have seen, an important amount (almost half) is reflected. As Geiger has said: 'If our eyes could see infra-red, then the shadow of trees would appear no longer green, but infra-red'.

As a result of these peculiar properties in relation to radiation, and also as a result of evaporation – by which each gram of water evaporated consumes from 570–600 calories, according to the temperature – the temperature becomes close to that of the air when the sky is overcast, and again when the plant is completely shaded by other plants.

Figure 5. Meadow grass (continuous line) reflects light selectively, according to its wave-length; a dead surface such as concrete (dashed line) is a more uniform reflector (after F. Sauberer).

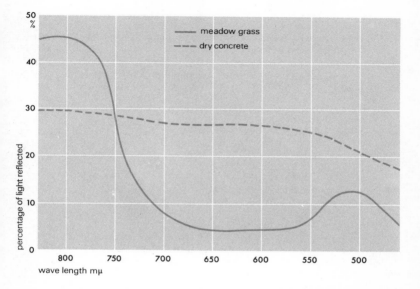

Further progress can be made by measuring with very fine thermo-electric needles the temperature on the surface of the leaves. It evidently depends on the degree of exposure of the leaf, but also on the botanical species, and always lies somewhere between the temperature of the soil and that of the surrounding air. Huber has constructed curves which show in striking fashion how the fleshy leaves of *Echinocactus* approach more nearly to the temperature of the soil, whereas the narrower leaves of *Lactuca* are closer to that of the air.

Waggoner and Shaw (1950) have studied the temperature of the leaves of potato and tomato. In the sun their temperature may lie from 3–8°C above that of the surrounding air; but in the shade they fall to 0·8°C below. Moreover differences up to 3°C can be found between leaves that lie in line with the sun's rays and leaves that are at right angles. This must obviously be taken into account if one is

Table 1 Effect of radiation on the temperature of various insects (after Masek Fialla).

Thermometer painted black reads 32°		Temperature of insect	Temperature of air	Difference
Bombus	In sunlight	37·5	26	+11
Xylocopa	,,	35	,,	+ 9
Apis	,,	31	,,	+ 5
Anisoplia	,,	29	,,	+ 3
Asilus	,,	28·5	,,	+ 2·5
Damselfly	,,	28·3	,,	+ 2·3
Butterfly	,,	27	,,	+ 1
Butterfly	In shade	25·5	,,	− 0·5
Damselfly	,,	26	,,	0

studying, for example, leaf-miners; they pass their entire life, not only inside leaves, but often within a single layer of the leaf, the palisade-tissue, for example; the difference between the temperature of the air and that of the plant can be as much as 11°C in the case of fleshy leaves, and rises even higher in the case of the magnolia. Temperatures higher than 56°C have been recorded on the surface or in the interior of leaves. Here is a little world far removed from our own, but it is the world of a great many insects, that of aphids for example.

One very interesting effect of radiation is that on the body temperature of insects. Don't forget that we are dealing with animals with variable temperatures (poikilothermic animals), whose powers of temperature regulation are nil, or very poor. They react differently therefore, according to their size, their way of life, their shape, and their colour (table 1).

In caterpillars of *Vanessa urticae* the temperature of the body may rise in the sun up to 39·9°C, even though the air-temperature does not go above 15·6°C. In contrast the temperature of both caterpillars and adult butterflies is close to that of the air at night, or on cloudy days. When *Vanessa* is in flight the double heating effect of muscular effort and solar radiation explains the presence of these butterflies in air at freezing-point at more than 4,000 metres altitude in the Caucasus.

Tiny species such as *Erebia aethiops*, however, are incapable of such feats. Because their surface area is so much bigger in proportion to their size, they lose so much heat that they can only fly by utilising the heat from the sun; muscular movement by itself does not raise their temperature high enough.

Details that at first sight seem trivial may have their effect on the distribution of temperatures. For example, it is well known that cold air is heavier than warm air; this is the principle of the hot-air balloon. As a result cold air flows like water down slopes, and forms pools wherever it is stopped by some obstacle. This happens on a miniature scale among the vegetation. For example Ulrich and Mäde recorded a drop of cold air inside a cactus leaf which had its edges curled up to form a receptacle; and it is easy to find other examples among plants of organs which have deep, hollow cavities, opening upwards, in which cold air collects. Organisms that hide in such places are enjoying a 'micro-ramification of their micro-universe'.

Microclimates in flowers

These are very special microclimates, varying with the form and colour of the flower, and the biotope formed by the cavities of deep flowers is of great interest. Budel (1957) has studied it in relation to temperature. Humidity, too, is greatly different in

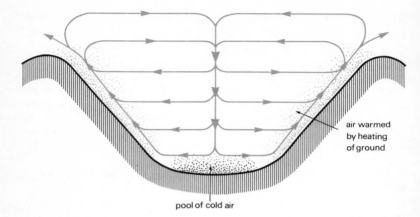

Figure 6. Cross-section of a valley, showing how the air circulates during the daytime. The sides of the valley become warm, and heat the air in contact with them, which rises. A return movement of colder air sinks down the middle of the valley, creating a 'pool' of cold air in the valley-bottom (after A. Wegener).

air warmed
by heating
of ground

pool of cold air

these cavities from what it is outside. Moreover, remembering that the flower is undergoing active metabolism, it is very likely that the enclosed air has a different composition from the air outside, though as far as I know no one has so far tried to analyse it. This could be important, because a great many insects are inhabitants of tubular flowers, and God knows what strange universe they could be living in down there without our knowing anything about it.

Kato, in 1943, had the idea of studying the microclimatic temperatures inside the actual blossom of a chrysanthemum. It is not simple, and at least three types of microclimate exist there. One type has a nearly uniform temperature all over the surface of the flower; in a second type the temperature is higher on the floral disc; and in the third the highest temperature is on the corolla, an effect that is difficult to understand.

Microclimates in forests

The biggest modification to the general climate of a region is brought about by the foliage of big trees, and I think this is an

Figure 7. The diurnal range of temperature inside a wood is always less than in open country. The effect is most marked during the summer months, and is more pronounced inside a deciduous wood than among evergreens, and among broad-leaved trees than among those with narrow leaves (after Müttrich).

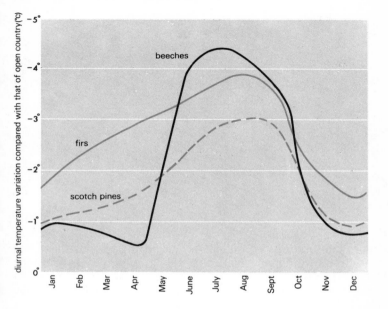

excellent example of a microclimate. Making a study of this has raised many problems of suitable equipment. It has been necessary to build platforms at heights of up to 25 metres, supporting meteorological instruments at regular distances from the ground upwards. The Germans have been doing this since 1927, but alas, the entomologists have not been able to climb the meteorologists' ladders! However some observations give the impression that the forest is to some extent a truly unexplored continent, as far as the 'world of the treetops' is concerned.

For obvious reasons the treetops are not a place where entomologists regularly operate, but we know that the climatic conditions that are met with there are extremely specialised, and not at all like the conditions found on the ground below: temperature, humidity,

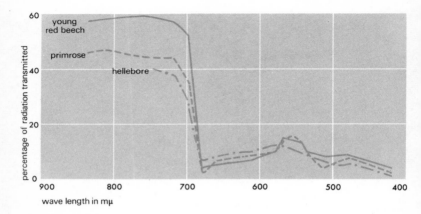

Figure 8. Leaves are selective in the wavelengths that they transmit, and there is some difference between the leaves of different plants.

rainfall, gain and loss of radiant heat, and the play of the winds are all totally different. Naturally this cannot fail to have its effect on the fauna up there. We know, for example, that certain species believed to be rare, only appear to be so because they normally live up in the treetops, and rarely come down to ground level. This is true of the beautiful Cetoniid beetle *Potesia speciosissima*, well known to amateur coleopterists, which lives high up in the treetops.

Let us look more closely at the climatic peculiarities of the forest. Perhaps the most characteristic of these is the balance of radiation. Forest insects, apart from those of the treetops, do not receive anything like the same radiation as those which live out in the open air. The orange component of the spectrum, for example, is reduced by 8% from its value in the open air. The green gets through easily, of course; that is why forests provide a green shade. The infra-red passes easily through the foliage, too, but on the whole, and even including the infra-red, the forest floor receives only a low percentage of the sun's radiation.

Evidently the mean radiation is significant, because there are

Figure 9. Inside a beech wood (trees 120–150 years old) light intensity falls off rapidly below the levels of the crowns. This effect is greater on a sunny day than on an overcast day, when the clouds scatter light into the shadows (after E. Trapp).

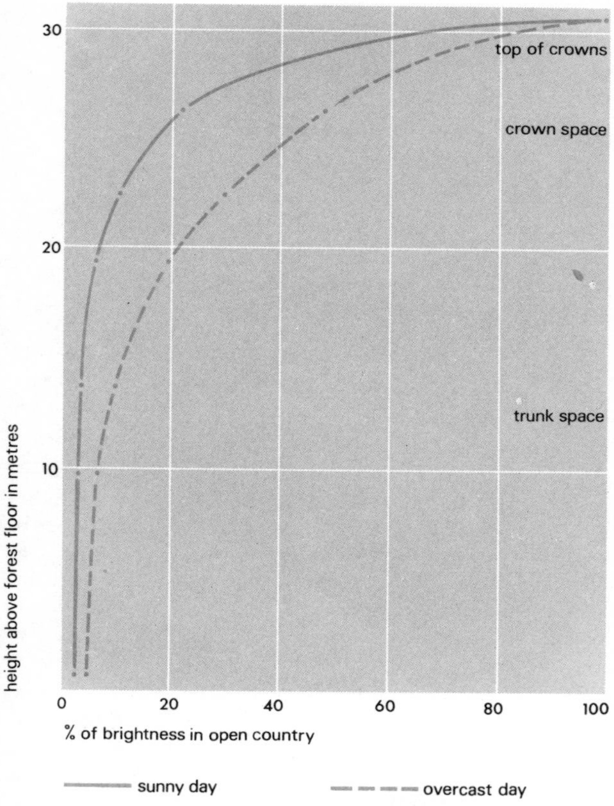

areas of very thick foliage, particularly dark, where the fauna and even the flora is heavily reduced. When the solar radiation is cut down below 16 % the forest floor remains bare. Between 16 and 18 % the first mosses begin to appear. Between 22 and 26 % we find bushes of bay and myrtle, but rather scattered. The radiation must rise

Figure 10. Progress of warming-up of a
mixed forest of oak and young beeches
in the three hours after sunrise.
The graphs show the rise of temperature
at various heights, as indicated in
the key (after R. Geiger and H. Amann).

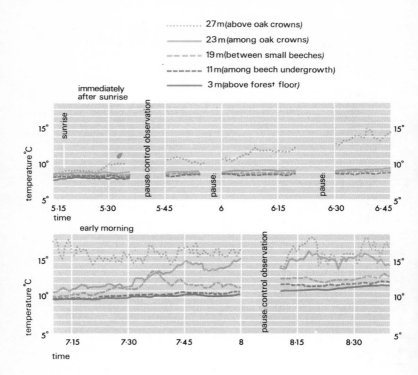

above 30% for the soil to become covered with vegetation.

The *temperature* of the air in forests, always lower than that of
the air outside, varies enormously from place to place. At sunrise
the coldest zone of an oak forest, for example, is to be found in the
vicinity of the crowns, 23 metres up; in contrast the warmest zone
is on the forest floor. As the sun rises in the sky the treetops warm
up quickly, and soon they are 5°C warmer than anywhere else,

Table 2 Wind speed at different levels in a pine-wood
(after Geiger).

Position of anemometer	Height in metres above ground level	Mean wind-speed in metres per sec
Above the treetops	16	1·61
At treetop level	13	0·90
In the canopy	10	0·69
Upper part of trunk	7·40	0·67
At middle level	4·25	0·69
Forest floor	1	0·60

where the chill of the night still lingers. It is not until after seven o'clock in the morning in summer that the gradual warming up of the interior of the wood brings the insect world to life; we must wait until the sun has been up at least three hours before the layer nearest to the ground begins to warm up in its turn.

In the middle of the day, nevertheless, it will be the treetop layer that will remain the warmest, since the underwood, having quickly reached its equilibrium, will maintain it with remarkable consistency throughout the day. During the night the temperature will stay very uniform all through the forest, with two zones of minimum temperature, one on the forest floor, where the heavier cold air sinks, and the other, unexpectedly, in the treetops. Selzer noted this, but no good explanation is known.

Humidity is great in the forest, obviously as a result of the relatively low temperature, and also of the little movement of air between the tree-trunks. Dew does not fall there, or hardly any; it is confined to the treetop zone, but there it is so heavy that several hours of sunshine are necessary to evaporate it. Later in the day humidity arises from two sources, from the treetops, where transpiration is intense, and also from the soil of the forest.

It is instructive to note that the temperature only rises slightly as one moves closer to the forest floor, whereas the humidity rises considerably, especially if there is a covering of vegetation; and this humidity cannot but increase towards evening, as a result of the uninterrupted transfer of water brought about by the transpiration in the treetops. It can be found, as Geiger did, that there is more than 25 % difference between the humidity close to the ground and that just at treetop level.

Wind and rain are greatly reduced, as far as this can be recorded. Geiger placed six anemometers in a pine-wood for a period of 188 hours, and obtained the figures listed in table 2 on page 29.

This shows once again, if this is needed, that the insects of the treetops do not live in at all the same environment as those which move about on the ground. The wind conditions also can be appreciated, and with more precision if that is possible, by measuring the number of hours of calm, when the anemometer is at rest, inside an oak wood (table 3, page 33).

It is much more difficult to appreciate the importance of rainfall, because of the effect of interception by the foliage, for which Clarke, as we have already seen, invented his 'interceptometer'. But this apparatus was intended for the measurement of interception of rain by small plants in cultivated fields. The problem is much more complicated in forests because of the extreme irregularity of the canopy. It is no use putting a rain gauge in the forest and then comparing it with a rain gauge outside. Enormous differences can be recorded even one metre away, so that Hoppe declared that what was recorded by a rain gauge in a forest had no relation to what was falling outside, at least when a light or moderate rain was falling.

Hoppe used a series of twenty rain gauges, equally spaced and

Figure 11 (*top*). Above bare ground, the wind-speed increases with
height, and at all heights the speed is generally greatest
in the middle of the day (after C. Hellman).
Figure 12 (*bottom*). In a pine-forest the relative humidity is always greater
just above the forest floor than it is above the crowns of the trees.
The difference between the two situations is greatest in late afternoon.

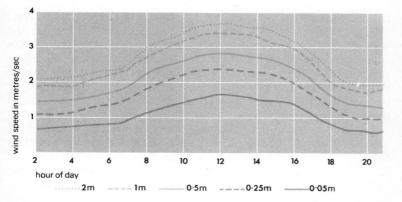

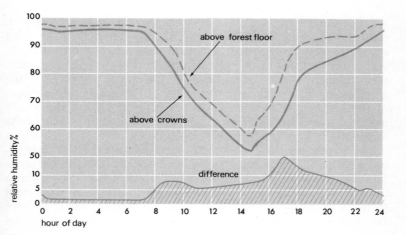

laid out in two lines at right angles. In a pine-forest, this method indicated that two-thirds of the rain did not reach the ground and was retained in the canopy. This was for a light shower; yet it is curious to note that even in the most violent and prolonged downpour a fifth of the rain never reached the soil, in particular near to the trunks. This can be seen in table 4, which gives the percentage of total precipitation that reached the soil, as a percentage of the precipitation outside.

Under deciduous trees the percentage of rain that reaches the ground is much greater. This might seem surprising, since the foliage is denser than it is in a pine-forest, but while the rain remains in drops on the pine-needles, it runs down the broad leaves of deciduous trees, and flows down the branches. This happens so effectively that the amount of rain to reach the ground may exceed 50%, even in very light rain. The water running down the trunk amounts to one fifth of the total, whereas less than 5% runs down the trunk of the pine.

The microclimate of clearings, copses and borders

A large number of insects live in clearings, and are never met with elsewhere, and so it is of the greatest importance to understand clearly the conditions that obtain in this micro-universe. First, everything depends on the size of the clearing. If it is very small, then the microclimate does not differ materially from that of the surrounding forest, except, naturally, in the greater penetration of the sun's rays. The bigger the clearing, the more the breeze penetrates, and the air is no longer heavy and still, as it is in the forest and in very small clearings.

The important thing is not the mere diameter of the clearing, but what relation this bears to the height of the surrounding trees. Lanscher has even proposed a formula which makes it possible to calculate the radiations reflected by the clearing, an important factor in its microclimate, if one knows the relative humidity of the air in the clearing and the angles at which the treetops are seen by

Table 3 Number of hours of calm at different levels in an oak wood (after Geiger).

Position of anemometer	Height above ground in metres	% of hours of calm	
		trees not in leaf	trees in leaf
Above canopy	27	0	10
In canopy	24	8	33
At base of canopy	20	35	86
Above ground	4	67	98

Table 4 Interception of rain by pine-trees (after Hoppe).

Distance from the trunk in metres	0 to $\frac{1}{2}$	$\frac{1}{2}$ to 1	1 to $1\frac{1}{2}$	over $1\frac{1}{2}$	near to a clearing
% of precipitation reaching the soil	55	60	63	66	76

an observer stationed at the centre of the clearing. Air-movement is small when the clearing is not very big, and Swedish observers were the first to show that then its climate is more extreme than that outside, with greater maxima and minima.

Schubert, during the months of August and September, found 9·4°C temperature range between the trunks in a forest, 9·9°C outside, but 10·8°C under a screen in the middle of a clearing. In table 5 (page 34) Geiger gives a series of figures that are revealing.

In contrast, the temperature at night falls more rapidly than the

Table 5 Rainfall and temperature in clearings (after Geiger).

Diameter of clearing in metres	0	12	22	24	38	47	87
Rainfall in clearing compared with that outside forest		87%			105%		102%
Excess of temperature compared with forest at midday	0	0·7	1·6	2	3·2	5·4	4·1

diameter increases. This is a result not only of radiation losses, which also increase more rapidly than the diameter of the clearing, but also from the fact that in small clearings the cold air mixes with the warm air among the nearby tree trunks; whereas in the big clearings the air which has been cooled above the treetops sinks down into the clearing. This is what Geiger has called 'the night wind of the forest'.

Meteorological phenomena are still more complex on the *margins* of woods. It must be realised that the woodland, a zone of calm, is surrounded by a belt of temperature disturbances that are quite abrupt. Lacour noted this in 1872. This arises from an increase in the mean level of radiation, which itself is a paradoxical consequence of the fact that air close to the woodland boundary is still. The mean total of rainfall close to the boundary may also be either increased or decreased by the proximity of the trees, which act in some ways like a ridge of higher ground. It is to be expected, therefore, that the plants, and even more the insects, will be different, not only inside the wood, but also on its margins, from those to be found right outside.

In addition there are the forest winds, of which an example was given above. The very fact that the forest presents an obstacle to the air-currents forces these to be deflected upwards, so effectively

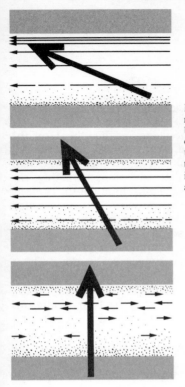

Figure 13. Air movements in a forest clearing, represented diagrammatically by two parallel belts of trees. The broad arrow shows the direction of the wind above the tree-tops and the smaller arrows the wind in the clearing, the closeness of the arrows giving an indication of the wind-strength; the stippled areas are zones of still air (after Geiger).

that the forest-fringe is left with a calm belt about half as broad as the height of the trees. During the day the layer of air close to the ground in the open country warms up, but the corresponding layer inside the woodland remains cold; whereupon this cold air flows outwards, as the 'diurnal forest wind'. It is comparable to the sea-breeze, which blows during the day from the cool sea-surface towards the warmer land, and, in the striking phrase of Schmauss (1920), is a 'sea-breeze without a sea'.

As for the 'night wind of the forest', mentioned earlier, that is a wave of cold air which flows, in this case, from the canopy of the trees into open spaces on the ground. Kochl studied it by releasing small balloons, and recorded that its velocity may reach one metre per second. It is much stronger than this on a wooded slope, and may flow down towards the bottom of the valley at 3 metres per second.

Yet, as Geiger emphasises, our knowledge of the climate of the forest fringe is still too meagre. 'We do not know, for example', he says, 'whether the same marginal belt is warmer all the year round, or whether there are seasonal variations; whether the driest edge is always the warmest, and the most humid is the coolest; if the temperature and humidity of the ground are always in step with the microclimate of the ground-layer, or whether they also vary with the macroclimate . . . and so on'.

The litter of dead leaves provides a habitat for a great range of woodland insects. Certain entomologists specialise in the study of this biotope, and of the underlying soil – and they are dismayed at the magnitude of their task. First of all, the chemical composition of the leaves varies according to whether they are from coniferous or deciduous trees. The acidity of deciduous leaves is greater, that is the pH is lower; on the other hand pine needles decompose more quickly. Finally the rain which reaches the soil after leaching the leaves on the trees has been changed chemically, and in particular it has become richer in mineral salts. It may contain 4–20 times as much calcium, 10–50 times as much potassium, as the rain that falls on open ground. Taum calculated that underneath a plantation of *Pinus sylvestris* and spruce, six weeks of rain (100 mm) had brought to the soil 2–4 kg per hectare of calcium, sodium and potassium.

All this helps to modify profoundly the litter of dead leaves, and the insects living there cannot fail to be affected by it.

The microclimate of open fields and low herbage

This has been magnificently studied by German workers, who before anyone else realised the importance of a better understanding of the process of *cultivation*; a practice which man has been engaged in for at least five thousand years, without really understanding what he was doing. The soil is periodically worked and

Figure 14. Temperatures in the air above a field of Jerusalem artichokes, from ground level up to a height of one metre, during one day, 4 August 1935. During two periods (about 5–8 hours, 18–21 hours) air temperature was almost uniform up to this height, but during the rest of the day cells of warm and cold air formed (after A. Mäde).

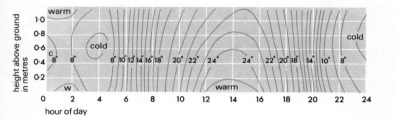

turned over to some depth, bringing about enormous changes in the physical condition of the soil and in its fauna. Most of all, man creates a state of affairs that is very rarely found in nature, that is to say *an almost completely homogeneous vegetation*, sometimes over very great areas.

To some extent this simplifies the problems, because every plant has its own relationship with the local climate, and it is much easier if only one such relationship needs to be considered. This applies even more forcibly to the fauna, as we shall see later on.

The *cultivated field* sets complex problems, depending on whether the general direction of growth of the vegetation is *upwards*, as in cereal crops, or *horizontal* as in meadow plants, turnsole (*Crozophora tinctoria*), or Jerusalem artichoke. There are also fundamental differences in the distribution of radiation and temperature.

Perhaps the most difficult factor to understand, as Geiger has said, is the 'economy of radiations' in the field. The relation between incident and reflected radiation follows complex laws. In a cornfield the incident radiation 50 cm above ground is hardly reduced, even though the long stems of wheat may reach or exceed this height; but at 10 cm above the ground it is only one quarter of that above the level of the plants. Down on the ground it is only one fifth.

If we go from this to a field of clover, then the interception is very much greater, and almost total 10 cm above the ground. In addition the warmer parts of the plants radiate towards the cooler, or reflect a certain percentage of the radiation that falls on them,

Figure 15. Gradual absorption of radiation in a meadow. The maximum
radiation falling on to the tops of the plants, and on to the bare ground
outside, is represented by the figure 1·08. The vertical lines represent
graphically the number of plants of that height in the mixed vegetation,
and the figures 1·04, 0·28, 0·19 the relative values of the radiation
which penetrates down to this level from above (after Ångström).

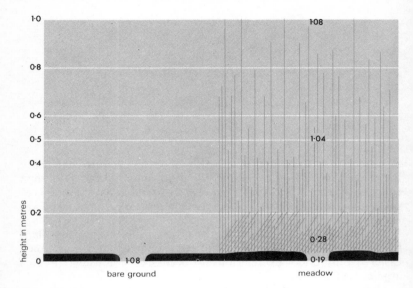

varying with the nature of the plant and the reflecting power of the
surface of its leaves.

What is difficult for a non-specialist to grasp is that, in spite of
the profound difference in the nature of their surfaces, a square
metre of bare soil radiates at night the same amount as a square
metre that is covered with vegetation. The difference lies in the
balance of heat gained or lost. In the case of bare soil all the exchanges take place at the surface, where air and soil meet, whereas
over a crop the exchanges are spread through a layer of varying
depth. As a result the distribution of temperatures is quite different
in the interior of this carpet of vegetation, and once again varies
with the constituent plants.

When the plants have interlocking leaves, like those of a field of
clover, the horizontal plane of the flowers captures the most
radiation; this is the warmest zone during the day, and it is this

The 'dew-balance' is one of the
delicate instruments necessary
in the study of microclimates.
The balance registers the weight
of the dew which falls on a
disc of known area.

which radiates most during the night. Geiger considers that planting
in rows notably encourages the growth of the young plants. In
June, the clover shoots are still not greatly developed, and the sun's
rays still reach the soil, which then in its turn radiates to the plants,
which find themselves beyond their optimum temperature. But in
August the plants 'join hands', in the picturesque phrase of Geiger,
that is to say adjacent shoots interlock; whereupon the microclimate changes abruptly, the temperature comes nearer to the
optimum, and plant growth shows a sudden spurt. It is inevitable
that this must apply equally to the insects that live in the clover,
and that is why it is important to us.

The light is intercepted to an increasing extent by wheat, rice,
barley and oats; among legumes, beans stop more light than
vetches or peas (Konold & Hohendorf, 1944).

The effect of the *colour of the soil* on the microclimate and hence on the growth of vegetation, has been brought to the fore by some odd observations. In Italy, for example, charcoal is scattered among the vines to speed up the melting of the snow. The crop of tomatoes, espalier fruits or vines can be increased by painting white the wall behind them; conversely, painting the wall black stimulates the woody growth of the plant at the expense of the fruit. In Rumania it has been said that covering the soil with white paper may double the crop of certain kinds of tomatoes.

The importance of twilight and daybreak

This is not directly relevant to our subject, since the gradual coming of day, and its progressive fading into darkness have never been given special consideration by ecologists. When animals, insects or mammals, are reared in the laboratory it is usual to switch the light on or off abruptly, but how do we know this has no effect on the biology or the development of the subjects? It would be rash to say so after the work of Kawanaul on mice. He maintains that it is difficult to change the nocturnal rhythm of mice if the periods of light and darkness are varied by a timeswitch, but if the illumination is changed gradually it is much easier to change the rhythm of the animals. How does this affect insects? Without a doubt in these animals, which are more dependent on external conditions than are mice, the importance of twilight and of daybreak must be still greater, but no experiments have yet been made.

Microclimates for insects living in beans

Labeyrie and Maison (1954) have explained in a very interesting way, in terms of the microclimate, the differences in distribution of the bruchid beetle of beans (*Acanthoscelides obsoletus*) in fields of maize; beans and maize are cultivated together in the Landes District of France. The maize quickly outgrows the beans; temperature and humidity differ only a little between the centre of the field and its perimeter. Nevertheless infestation by the beetles is always much greater on the perimeter of the field, and increases with distance from the ground, reaching a maximum at the upper level of the plants. Among beans without maize, on the contrary, the infestation decreases with height. In the middle of a big field the authors pulled up the maize over 25 square metres, leaving only beans there, whereupon in this 'clearing' infestation was four times as great as it was under a maize cover. The bean crop was a dwarf haricot.

This last arrangement, with a 'clearing' of beans in the middle of a sea of maize, shows that the maize is not acting as a mechanical obstacle to the movement of the beetles, but it does form a barrier to the penetration of sunlight, only 20% of which gets through. Now beneath withered maize the interception of sunlight is much less, and the infestation of beetles shows a corresponding increase. Labeyrie & Maison think, therefore, that these fluctuations in beetle-population are due mainly to variations in radiation.

The German meteorologist Filzer made a methodical comparison between a plant with its foliage vertical: maize, and a horizontal plant: turnsole, with variations of surface and density of planting: areas of surface ninety, sixty-four and forty-five square centimetres; density expressed by distance between plants of 8·6, 6, 4·2 cm. The differences he found during four fine days in September between the surface of the soil and a point situated one metre above ground level are listed in table 6 on page 42.

The more the plants are packed together, and the greater the area that they occupy, the cooler is the layer of air close to the soil, and the more definite is the characteristic microclimate. The highest temperatures arise whenever the density is low, but for a medium density this rise of temperature occurs only if the surface of the seedlings is small.

At night the readings are a little different, and there is not the same apparent relation between density and surface of the seed-lings and the temperature. The air is then warmer close to the soil than at a height of one metre, but it is at the summit of the plants of clover that the maximum temperature is found. At night the air

Table 6 Temperature of soil compared with that at one metre above ground, under two different crops (after Filzer).

Density of vegetation	Turnsole			Maize		
	Great	Medium	Low	Great	Medium	Low
Large area	−3	−1·8	+0·5	−2·5	−0·4	+3·7
Medium area	−1·7	−0·7	+0·9	−	−	−
Small area	−0·6	+0·2	+3·6	−1·2	+1	+3·2

cools rapidly in the floral zone, but its density increases, and it promptly flows down to the foot of the stems; it is there, as a result, the lowest night-time minimum is recorded. In a field of rye, on the contrary, the leaves form close to the soil a very dense barrier of vegetation, which makes air movement very nearly impossible, so that the cold air from above can flow downwards hardly or not at all. This is so effective that the night-time minimum is to be found in this case halfway down the stems, and the daytime maximum close to the soil, where the warmth accumulates. Study is needed of the micromigrations of insects, in the different layers of vegetation, to see if they follow the nocturnal variations of microclimate as they do those of the daytime.

It is not possible here to review all the German research into the microclimate of cultivated fields, which has been carried out on almost all the vegetable crops that are cultivated in Germany. Fleischman has even proved that each species of insect on cereals has its own microclimate.

In the tropics the phenomena taking place in a cultivated field do not seem to be very different from those we experience in temperate countries in the summer, except that they are 'exaggerated'. Everything is changed when crops are irrigated, as is the case

Figures 16 and 17. Curves showing the vertical distribution of temperature (top) and relative humidity (bottom) at sunrise, and again at midday, in fields of sugar cane 2·5 m high, millet 1·5 m high, and open, uncultivated land (after L. A. Ramdas, R. J. Kalamka and K. M. Gadre).

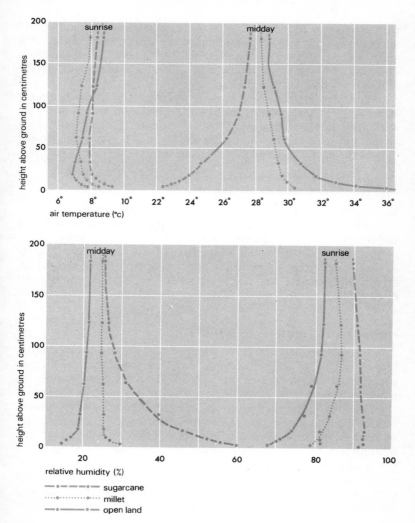

with cane-sugar in India, where it has been studied by Ramdas and his colleagues. While around mid-day the temperature in the open air may reach 36°C, it does not exceed 22°C at the foot of the canes of sugar. At night the temperature all along the stems hardly differs from that outside the crop.

In contrast, *in arctic regions* such as Greenland, it may be most important for the plants to make the maximum use of the heat available during the day. Wegener stated that in north-east Greenland the temperature in the middle of the plants can exceed that of the air by eight or nine degrees, and in one case even 16°C.

The microclimate in vineyards

Vineyards present a complicated microclimate, because there is a shrubby crop where the sun not only beats on the foliage, but still has free access to the soil between the plants. The temperature of the soil thus rises much above that of the vines. At night the coolest zone is to be found at the upper extremity of the root-stock, at the point where the plant branches out, and which is most favourable to the formation of dew on the leaves.

Humidity in relation to wind

The impression given by the reading of humidity and temperature in the middle of a field is quite different from that which one experiences when one goes into a wood. It is much warmer in the wood than it is outside, among the field-plants, and the humidity is greater there. In practice, on the one hand the mass of vegetation retains the heat of the soil, and on the other there is much radiation of heat from the leaves and branches. The same is true of the humidity. The vegetational cover inhibits the evaporation of moisture from the soil, while at the same time enormous transpiration from the leaves augments the moisture in the air. Stocker, for example, noted in a pasture near Freiburg on 18 July, 57% relative humidity at a height of one metre above the ground; 78% at a height

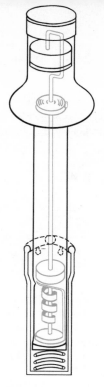

Figure 18. Goillot's microhygrometer, for measuring the humidity in micro-environments. Moving parts are shown in green, fixed parts in black (after Chauvin, 1957).

of 13 cm among the leaves of clover, and 96% in the grass 2 cm above the soil. But the development of this great gradient of humidity is not paralleled in the thermal gradient. In fact the thermal strata become inverted every day. The soil, which gives up warmth to the air during the day, receives it back from the air during the night, but the thermal gradient is nearly the same by day and by night.

Evaporation from soil that is covered with vegetation is twice as great as it is from bare soil, and may increase to eight times, at least for a very short time. The retention of this mass of water vapour is greater in proportion to the density of the vegetation, as Filzer showed clearly in a wheat-field where the seedlings were sown at three different densities (table 7, page 46).

At the surface of the vegetation the readings of humidity are extremely irregular because 'bubbles' of moist air rise from the

Table 7 Retention of water vapour by crops of different density
(after Filzer).

Density of vegetation	Great	Medium	Low	Bare soil
Square cm of leaf-surface per cc of air	1·81	0·82	0·38	0
Relative humidity	73	64	51	41

middle of the field and mix with the surrounding air. And all the time, the hygrometer never reaches saturation point. Wegener has recorded 98 % among leafy plants after rain, and this seems to be the highest humidity ever reached. In practice, as soon as evaporation begins, the evaporating surface is cooled, and this automatically reduces the intensity of the phenomenon.

In very dry and very hot regions it is the thermal effect which predominates, and humidity no longer shows the same distribution. At the edge of the desert, even among the leaves of the plants, the humidity is not much greater than round about, and sometimes it is even lower. This derives, according to Stocker, from the fact that the sun warms the plants excessively, and that the very dry wind of the desert extracts from them all trace of moisture.

For *hot, humid climates*, unfortunately, we have little data. In a field of millet that was not irrigated the humidity was a little greater close to the soil; it was much greater, naturally, in a field of sugar-cane which had irrigation. At night the differences from the external air tended to disappear.

Watering has a curiously lasting effect on the humidity of crops, according to Trappenberg (1932). In a tobacco field a spraying corresponding to 2–3 mm on a summer's morning was enough to raise the humidity appreciably throughout the day. A prolonged

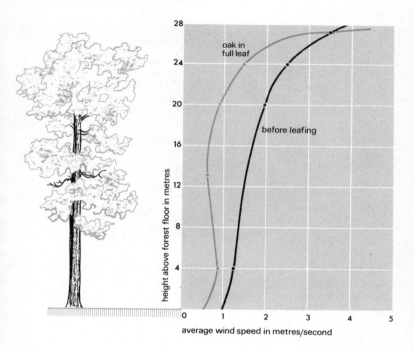

Figure 19. Inside a mixed forest of oak and young beech the wind speed increases rapidly as the level of the crowns is reached. The effect is accentuated when the trees are in full leaf (after Geiger and Amann).

watering, but at a low density (2 mm per hour) is more effective than a short intense soaking (20 mm in one hour).

When the tobacco field was watered very intensively all the extremes were moderated, particularly in temperature.

Obviously all this cannot fail to have its effect on the insects, and Lepointe (1964) saw this clearly when by watering he imitated the effects of rain on conifers such as juniper, cypress and yew. Especially in times of drought, after watering there is an abrupt increase in numbers of the insects, just as there is after rain. On juniper this population build-up begins after twenty-four hours,

Table 8 Attenuation of wind velocity inside tufts of *Calluna*

Height	Wind speed
At 180 cm above *Calluna*	9·3 m/sec.
At 50 cm, level with top of *Calluna*	3·7 m/sec.
At 30 cm, among *Calluna*	1·4 m/sec.

Table 9 Attenuation of wind velocity by different crops

Wind velocity m/sec	Wheat field	Bean field	Potato field
Less than 1	24%	20%	30%
From 1 to 2	15%	23%	24%
From 2 to 3	11%	15%	23%
More than 3	9%	11%	—

strange to say. Lepointe suggests that the watering at first drives away the insects that like water little or not at all, but that later the intense evaporation of moisture attracts all the moisture-loving insects round about.

As for the wind, this is very much damped down by vegetation, and this is a great part of the cause of the retention of warmth and humidity in the interior of a cultivated field or among low-growing plants. Stocker has recorded (table 8) the values for this attenuation of wind in the interior of tufts of the small heath (*Calluna*).

He concluded from this that a great many low-growing plants, when they are growing close together, are in fact never exposed to winds greater than one metre per second, and most of the time the winds they experience do not exceed 0·1 m/sec. The amount to which the wind is attenuated differs according to the nature of the plant, as would be expected and as Krentz has shown (table 9).

There are other bioclimatic factors which biologists have never taken into account: *electrical factors*. For generations, in so far as biologists have taken readings in the field, they have measured only temperature and sometimes humidity. As for measuring the total solar radiation, this was exceptional, and it was unthinkable to address oneself to measuring ionisation, and the incidence of atmospheric potential. Nevertheless these are phenomena that are neither more nor less mysterious than temperature, and there are good reasons for thinking that they must affect insects.

Edwards comments, for example, that the ionisation of the air modifies flight activity in *Calliphora*. An increase in the number of ions first brings about an increase in activity, which later returns to normal, even though the insects remain exposed to the ions. All the same it is only known to apply when these changes are positive, and nothing is detected if they are negative. In the aphid *Myzus persicae* (Haine, 1960) moulting is affected by an increase of negative ions, or a big drop in positive ions. In this context it must not be forgotten that the wind has more or less effect on atmospheric ionisation: for example a special kind of wind in certain Alpine countries, the föhn, provokes quite a few physiological disturbances; now, this wind is very rich in positive ions.

Another reason why insects should be highly sensitive to electrical conditions is that they become charged in the course of flight, and in this Edwards found the principle of a very original method of measuring flight activity. If the insects are placed in a metal cage which is earthed, they accumulate while in flight a positive charge big enough to register on an electrometer in the middle of the cage. Then the number and amplitude of the deflections of this instrument will provide a measure of the flight activity of the insect.

The gradient of potential has been completely neglected hitherto. However, everyone knows that the atmospheric potential falls rapidly in the first few metres above ground level. From the work of the physician Vlès we know that this factor has an effect on plants, so why should it not also affect insects? Edwards was the first to show that it does have such an effect. For example, the flight of *Drosophila* is temporarily abruptly reduced by sudden exposure to a potential gradient of 10–62 volts per cm. The period during which this activity is so reduced can be prolonged by reversing the polarity every five minutes. In *Calliphora* under the same circumstances the reduction of activity is shorter, and a steeper potential gradient is required.

It was Lepointe (1964) who demonstrated in the field the importance of a gradient of potential in ecology. He enclosed a juniper plant in a Faraday cage, and after repeatedly earthing and isolating the cage he measured the number of insects that took refuge in the foliage. When the cage is earthed the potential difference between it and the soil is eliminated, and *the fauna of the juniper plant becomes more than three times as great*. The build-up is rapid, and follows quickly after the electrical connection is made. *Oribates* (a genus of mites) is particularly sensitive to a potential gradient, and spiders are almost indifferent to it.

The *composition of the air* is not necessarily the same in the middle of a thick canopy of vegetation as it is in the open air. Back in 1951 Tonzig compared the composition of the air 40 metres above the ground, and in fields of wheat and of clover. In the atmosphere of cultivated fields the carbon dioxide fell to a minimum in the middle of the day, and reached a maximum between midnight and six a.m. At 28°C photosynthesis is very active, and the carbon dioxide content very low; but at higher temperatures still the assimilation of carbon dioxide decreases, respiration increases, and the proportion of CO_2 in the atmosphere goes up rapidly. In a field of beetroot studied by Reinau (1954) the CO_2 remained at about 0·03 parts per thousand, but with a series of quick jumps after midnight, which have not yet been explained.

The microclimate in laboratory experiments

In the laboratory, even under conditions that are thought to be well isolated from their surroundings, the presence of the animals in itself is enough to create a microclimate. For example, jars of flour in which *Tribolium confusum* and *Tribolium castaneum* are being reared maintain a higher temperature than similar jars, with the same amount of flour, but no insects. Three hundred larvae can raise the temperature in this way by 0·6°C above that of control jars without larvae. When a population of *Tribolium* is introduced into fresh flour a sudden rise of temperature is first produced, which builds up to a maximum in twenty-four hours, followed by a slight fall; and for six days the temperature remains at a higher level than that in the control jar.

Furthermore, account must be taken of the fact that the establishment of this microclimate depends on the distribution of the insects, and reaches a very different equilibrium according to the species of insects, the food material, and the temperature. Moreover, there occurs a nocturnal migration from the top of the jar downwards, which also influences the temperature (Pimentel, 1958).

English entomologists at Rothamsted Experimental Station have even used a balloon to lift their suction traps into the upper atmosphere.

2 Counting populations

We are surrounded, therefore, by a multitude of insects. They live in an infinite number of little worlds, interlocked within our own, and under conditions which, as we have just seen, may sometimes be very different from those with which we are familiar.

An entomologist eventually reaches the point where he is no longer content to capture insects at random, in order to add them to his collection. *He now wants to count them.* This preoccupation with numbers is a relatively recent one, which arose at the same time as modern developments in agriculture. The demand for ever-increasing yields led to the use not only of fertilisers, but also of insecticides. In the beginning it was thought that the situation was simple, and that the problem was in hand, while all the time we did not know enough to ask the right questions. One simple dusting ought to be enough to clear the fields of their pests at will. Then it became apparent that one treatment was not enough, that two were needed, then three, and sometimes many more; this was the situation among fruit-growers, who had to grow their crop under an almost unending cloud of insects. A reason was sought for these swarms of insects, which could not be brought under control by simple methods, and this showed up the complexity of the problem. We became aware of a whole series of new phenomena, and of serious gaps in our knowledge. 1 We did not know – and still are partly ignorant of – the exact laws of distribution of insects, for example in a field. Why are there more insect pests round the edges than in the middle? 2 We did not know how a population builds up from the moment when the first insect pests come out of the herbage and begin to attack the plants. 3 These unanswered questions stem from a still more fundamental lack of knowledge. *We did not know how to count the insects*: i.e. how to catch them conveniently, and in such a way that the number caught shall be strictly proportional to the total number present. Until there is exact information about numbers it is almost impossible to estimate the results of insecticidal treatment; and this can be seen from the contradictory conclusions of the older authors, whose disputes were backed up on both sides by equally inadequate techniques.

We are not considering at this point the resistance that insects can develop to insecticides, which is the subject of our final chapter. For the present let us stick to the problems of insect populations.

The difficulties of measuring insect populations

Consider a bag filled with black balls and white balls, and let us try to estimate the proportion of white to black, without the labour of counting them one by one. If it can be assumed that the two colours are uniformly mixed, it will be enough to count the proportions in a few samples. One sample is not enough, for it may happen to consist of a local concentration of, say, black balls. The number of samples, and the number of balls in each, which are necessary to give a reliable estimate of the true proportions of the colours in the entire bag, can be arrived at by simple statistics.

Things would be simple if only populations of insects were distributed like the balls in the bag! Far from it; imagine, instead, that the bag of balls had not been shaken up to begin with, that is that the two colours were not distributed at random; that the black balls had a tendency to gather themselves together, apart from the white balls; that according to the time of day the white balls either rose to the top of the bag or sank to the bottom; and above all that the balls evaded the hand of the experimenter who tried to grasp them. You would then have only a feeble idea of the complications that beset anyone who tries to count insects in the field. It can easily be understood why it is so difficult to take a sample that will accurately represent the mean of a population about which hardly anything is known.

The first practical problem: *not to scare away the insects one wants to trap*. Even without knowing anything about the insects it is obvious that this is the first requirement. But how to know if one has succeeded? There is no strict formula. It is necessary to proceed by successive approximations, and we shall understand it better after a brief consideration of the oldest technique for studying the insects of low-growing plants, *the sweep net*.

This has been used by entomologists since time immemorial. It is like a butterfly net, but a little more robust, with a shorter bag, and with the light muslin replaced by a strong canvas. It is swept vigorously through the tops of the plants, and after several minutes the insects trapped in it are transferred to a container. Almost every order of insects is represented in such a catch, as well as many spiders. But does the fauna caught by the sweep net give a true picture of what is present on the vegetation that is being swept?

Clearly it does not, as can be realised at once by simple observation and common sense. First of all, as can easily be seen, a cloud of insects fly away, many as soon as the entomologist comes near, without waiting for the net to disturb them. A certain number of long-horned grasshoppers, for example, are extremely sensitive to vibrations, and endowed with excellent sight into the bargain. It is enough, therefore, that footsteps shake the ground, even very lightly, for the insects to be put to flight; and they are perfectly capable of noticing a moving object as big as a man several metres away.

Other insects, for example the Colza weevil, show a different kind of reaction; at the slightest disturbance they let themselves fall to the ground.

Finally, only the upper parts of the vegetation are reached by the sweep net. It is true that most insects live there, but all the same there are some at the base of the stems. In addition there are *micromigrations:* according to the time of day, or to weather conditions, certain species from the tops may descend to the middle, or even the base of the stems, and the chance of catching them in a sweep net varies with the hour, or even from minute to minute.

But some authors have gone further and tried to compare catches in the sweep net with those taken by another method. The general idea is to place a big cylinder over the plants and to suck out all the insects inside it, thus taking a sample of the local population. Truth to tell this method is difficult to carry out. In practice one is aware that the small or very small insects fall down between the bases of the stems and are difficult or impossible to retrieve. Nevertheless the criticisms that can be made of the cylinder method are less serious than the objections to the sweep net, and it is always interesting to compare techniques so different in principle.

Among other published work may be mentioned that of Van Romney on the fauna of *Lepidium alyssoides*; *there is no exact relationship* between catches made with the cylinder and those made with the sweep net.

Does it follow, then, that the sweep net is no good? Not necessarily. The net is useless for studying synecology, the interrelations of different insects, but it is of some use for studying autecology, the affairs of one species. We must now consider these two terms a little more.

By *synecology* is understood the study of the complete picture of the fauna of a plant, or of a given environment, and of the consequent interaction of its diverse elements. *Autecology* consists of the study of one species, together with its parasites and predators. Many research workers confine themselves to autecology, because it is much easier, and I would say more rewarding; that is to say that one can, by restricting one's work to one species, achieve spectacular successes more quickly. For instance, if only one species of insect is involved it is possible to find out the times at which it is active, the effect upon it of various meteorological factors, the positions it takes up on its plant host, and so on . . . and then one can use the sweep net in a standardised manner with a good chance of getting consistent results.

Synecology is clearly much more complex: here there is no universal method of catching which works for all insects, as we shall see in a moment. Many people blame synecologists for tackling such a difficult problem, and for studying 'important' and 'unimportant' insects all jumbled together. But it would be quite easy to demonstrate to these people where autecology goes wrong, simply that the insect that we study in isolation is not really isolated in nature. Of course we have already mentioned its parasites and predators, but the very environment in which it is found is itself affected by a number of factors, in particular by the presence of other insects. When making a study of aphids and their enemies it must not be forgotten that ants not only cultivate greenfly, but actively defend them against their enemies, as has recently been proved; and this behaviour completely alters the equilibrium between predators and prey. But this is a very special example.

The food supply of an insect may be endangered by the presence of too many insects of another kind, which may not directly harm the first species, but feed on the same plant, at a greater rate, or perhaps release poisonous or repellent substances. This is well shown by weevils in flour, and in one of the later chapters we shall describe the beautiful tale of experimental synecology that can be told about the 'jar of Tribolium'.

Many other examples could be given of the innumerable inter-actions that make up the material of synecology. They are so many, and so poorly understood that it is hard to know what is important and what is not. To consider one species in isolation from others, as does autecology, can only be a provisional step, and it is neces-sary to move on as quickly as possible to synecology.

Other ways of catching insects

After this long but necessary digression, let us come back to methods of capture. Since the sweep net is not good enough, how should this problem be tackled?

It is essential to abandon from the start any idea of a single solution appropriate for all insects, and in all situations. To begin with we must distinguish: 1 those which fly; 2 those which are found resting on plants; 3 those which run on the ground; 4 those which live in the soil.

Catching insects in flight. These are most complicated and must detain us for a moment. Different kinds of trap may be used, but

Left The mechanism of the suction trap. At the base of the trap there is a turbine, and above this an ingenious device which makes it possible to separate the catches made in successive periods of time. The pile of discs which can be seen on the centre spindle is released, one by one, at selected intervals by a clockwork mechanism. Beneath each disc as it falls are trapped the insects caught in the preceding period.

Right These huge suction traps are extremely light and can be easily moved about.

they must satisfy certain requirements, the first of which is that they should be perfectly neutral: that is, neither attract nor repel the insects. If not, then they will give a false picture of the local fauna, making it seem either richer or poorer than it really is.

One of the first pieces of apparatus to be used in serious studies was the *suction trap*, which was used simultaneously by the English and by myself. The English used a huge apparatus, higher than a man, with a big bell turned towards the sky. A powerful turbine sucked in everything coming close. Subsequently Taylor made ingenious improvements: for instance all the catches are collected in a vertical tube, and every hour a clockwork movement releases a metal disc which traps the catch of the previous hour. I saw this apparatus working at the great experimental station of Rothamsted in England, which produces many scientific papers. The number of small creatures that are sucked in by this apparatus is incredible.

What faults does it have? Very few. It seems clear that it is a method to use for demographic studies – the counting of populations. Perhaps one may express a few minor objections. The insects are not deaf, and it is possible that the noise of the fan may either attract or repel them. Southwood answered this criticism by making a long plastic tube leading from the fan into the vicinity of the bell, several metres away, and showing that this did not produce any difference in the number of insects captured. Roth pointed out that insects and many other animals show what is called *rheotropism*, that is they are sensitive to a current of air or of water. Some go with the current, some swim or fly against it. It is quite possible, for example, that certain insects may struggle and escape when they feel the strong suction of the trap, and how can allowance be made for this in the results of trapping? Roth made the ingenious proposal to stop and restart the trap every five or ten minutes. In this way the insects that had been scared away would have time to resume their former positions before the trap started again, and it would give a more accurate picture of their distribution: but this experiment has not been carried out.

For the rest, the suction trap is too big to be used in different layers of the vegetation. With the help of some of my students I have tried to replace this bulky apparatus with a series of smaller suction traps, which could quite easily be placed in different settings in a field of alfalfa, for example. But then there is a danger that among these obstacles the suction will be too weak.

Another practical objection may be difficult to overcome. These cumbersome suction traps need a source of electricity nearby, or else a generator. My pupils and I chose the second alternative because the work of an ecologist takes place in the open country, where electricity supplies are few and far between. I remember the astonishment of the peaceful farmers of the Seine-et-Oise when we arrived with an impressive amount of equipment, all of this in order to collect invisible flies into a vacuum-cleaner.

Sticky Traps. But suction traps are not very convenient to use. I remember an old experiment that I made in my youth: I wanted to insulate two wires to make an electric circuit, and I could think of nothing better than to paint them. From the electrical point of view that paint was only a moderately good insulator, but from the entomological point of view the results were much more interesting. I had left the wires to dry in my grandmother's garden, and what was my amazement to find them almost buried in a mass of countless midges, and other insects of all kinds! It was very simple, all the same, and after all I had done no more than spiders do to catch insects. I had made an artificial spider's web, and I repeated it a few years later when, with several of my students, I was painfully trying to lay the foundations of experimental ecology in France. A shameful situation, especially considering how backward this shows us to have been in comparison with other countries.

We therefore smeared glue copiously on to a square metre of

wire-netting, and made our way, floundering about through the field of alfalfa – I remember it was pouring with rain at the time – to hang it up on a pole several metres high. The mesh, stretched on a wooden frame, swung all night in a strong westerly wind, and when we took it down the following morning my students could not believe their eyes: the mesh was covered with a shell of gummed insects. I thought then that the game was won, and I looked forward pleasantly to the days to come: we should only need to arrive in a new locality, to hang up there our sticky frames, and to come back a week later, for example, to find collected for us a sample of insects perfectly representative of the fauna on the move in that area. The prospect seemed all the better because the glue (which, as we shall see later on is a very curious substance) retained its adhesive properties almost indefinitely, in sunshine or in rain.

Alas, it was not as easy as all that! Nothing is ever simple in nature, and especially in ecology. It was only many years later that I could refer the detailed study of sticky traps to an old friend and collaborator Maurice Roth. We started, Roth and I, by exposing in a field of alfalfa small metal frames which supported sticky threads of nylon. We chose threads because I still had in my mind the idea of imitating a spider's web, and also because threads were the only objects fine enough not to deflect the air. Certain very small insects, of weak flight, are carried more or less passively in the small, turbulent air-currents which are stirred up all the time close to the surface of the fields. If an object of any appreciable size is placed in position there, the air-currents weave round it in a complex way, depending on its shape, and carrying away with them many of the insects with which we are concerned. This is one of the principal objections to what are called passive traps, that is to say those that do not themselves attract the insects.

The results at first corresponded well with what we expected. We found many insects caught on the threads, and it was easy to soak them off with trichlorethylene and examine them at leisure.

Roth noticed straightaway that the insects showed little variety. They were all small or very small. Now the simplest observation, it may be just a few strokes of the sweep net over the surface of the alfalfa, showed that many other species were present, some of them very bulky. Either our traps did not catch them, or they got away again. We then had the idea of increasing the sticky surface by using not more metal traps, but a metal trellis brushed with glue. The number of captures at once increased enormously. Moreover, the number did not alter very much if we spread glue over a sheet of transparent plastic: that is to say that the number of insects lost by deflection of the air currents was not important in comparison with the possibilities of avoiding the sticky surface if it was not big enough. But this is not the last of it. The insects caught on the sticky sheet are always middle-sized or small, and we never saw the big ones, which could only be caught in the sweep net. And again, it was essential that the sheet was transparent; if it was opaque the number of captures dropped immediately. Under these conditions the shape of the trap was no longer unimportant, because it now became necessary to minimise the deflections of the air-currents. For example Roth used a sticky cone, which gave still better results than the sheets.

Moericke's Traps. Another method will catch a really astonishing number of insects. We owe it to the German biologist Moericke, who, it seems, discovered it by chance. It consists of setting out just above the vegetation coloured dishes containing a little water. A large number of insects fall in and drown themselves, provided always that the dishes are green or yellow. If they are white, or even merely have a white ring round them, the number caught falls considerably. No one knows the reason why white is repellent in this way. In any case, this shows that colour is important in sticky traps, too.

As far as I know no one has tried painting sticky traps white, but Roth showed that black sticky traps lost all their effectiveness. English authors found that they caught many more aphids if the sticky traps were yellow. This related, obviously, to the peculiarities of colour vision in insects, which have been studied by a great many people. Most insects see the spectrum visible to the human eye, except for red, which is confused with black by many Hymenoptera. And insects often have innate preferences, for example for yellow or yellow-green, and sometimes for blue. But as far as I know physiologists have never demonstrated any repellent effect of white; on the contrary white flowers like cow-parsley are attractive to a great many insects. It is true that what we see as white flowers do not appear white to insects because they reflect ultra-violet to a greater or lesser extent, and the great majority of insects see ultra-violet as a colour. Should one then conclude that the white of Moericke's traps did not reflect ultra-violet, or did so in some abnormal way? I do not know; but this shows how an ecological observation in nature requires research in physiology before it can be properly interpreted.

Other kinds of trap, using light or scent. Entomologists in the past, without any idea of getting statistical data, but solely to collect as many species as possible, tried out almost all the possible kinds of trap, and notably light traps, and traps using chemical attractants. It is only necessary to leave a lighted lamp in front of an open window to discover how effective light traps can be. And those of my readers who are old enough will perhaps remember those objects like a carafe without a bottom, but with a circular gutter, in which we put water and a spot of jam. Wasps, butterflies, bees and all sorts of other insects quickly came and drowned themselves.

Why shouldn't we, then, make use of these methods to take samples of insect populations? For the very simple reason that we are no longer dealing with a neutral trap, but with traps that have a positive, selective, action, attracting some kinds of insect, to the exclusion of others. They can therefore be used with precision in autecology, but definitely not in synecology. For example, light traps attract only insects that are photopositive, that is those which move towards a light. Now this is very far from being a characteristic of all insects. Many are photonegative. Even a photopositive species does not always behave in this way throughout its life. Or again, only one of the two sexes does so.

Another problem is to know from what distance the insects come to be caught; in other words, what is the radius of effective collecting.

But they have good points, and light traps, though useless for analyses of populations, still have brought to our notice some odd facts about the biology of moths, which may apply to other insects also. If the traps are placed at different heights above the ground, up to twenty metres, they collect different species, and the two sexes of one species may occur at different levels. Williams of Rothamsted made this curious observation. I can still recall him, with the diffident manner of the English scientist, and a delighted smile, showing everybody his catch for the night. It consisted of dishes full of grey Noctuid moths, which are active in the dark. His colleagues laughed, and called him 'Murderer'!

Taylor showed that among different species of night-flying moths there are really enormous differences in the percentage caught in light traps; some species are caught five thousand times as often as others. On the other hand for any one species, the efficiency of the trap suffers from considerable variations, which are unpredictable, and unexplained. In the case of *Agrochola lychnidis* the traps only begin to collect specimens when at least 10% of the moths are in flight, and then only if they are flying low, below three metres. But these are abnormal individuals of the species since 90% of *Agrochola* normally fly seven metres high.

Finally, it had not previously occurred to people to take any account of moonlight. Now according to Provost (1959) light traps catch six times as many mosquitoes or noctuid moths around new moon as at full moon, whereas suction traps do not show this kind of periodicity. Still more surprising are the observations of Robinson who placed his traps one hundred metres from one another in a biotope apparently uniform, and in open country. Nevertheless it often happened that the catches were completely different, both in composition and in numbers, even though an observer standing by one of the traps was within sight of several others. Does this mean that the distribution of populations of insects is so very irregular? This variation among traps placed less than one hundred metres apart has so far not received attention from research workers; when it does they will be forced to abandon an idea that they are all too ready to accept: the idea that ecology is a simple science . . .

Macleod (1962) found a similar irregularity when he used chemical traps. *Calliphora* came to baits in a very irregular fashion, even though they were only a few metres apart. It seems as if there are local congregations of these flies, but the cause is not yet clear.

The law of the minimum – the threshold

When traps are being used, such as light traps, it must be realised that the result depends on which of the various factors happens to be nearest to the *minimum requirement* for activity to begin. During every twenty-four hours daylight drops below this minimum at some point, and it is this which seems to have the biggest effect on the activity of insects. Humidity, temperature and the strength of the wind only affect the *extent* of this activity. If during certain weather conditions one or more of these factors remains below the minimum throughout the night, then the hunger of the moths becomes intense. The deterrent effect of light, which normally prevents them from flying by day is then overcome, and they begin flying about in brighter light than usual (Brolarsen, 1943). All this must be taken into account when tackling the often hopeless task of finding a correlation between the curve of activity and the variations of any single climatic factor.

Insects resting on plants – how can these be caught ?

There remains a very different problem, that of insects that do not fly about, either because they have no wings, or because they lie low when anyone goes near them. This problem looks simple,

Figure 20. The sampler in action (after Chauvin, 1956).

but is diabolically complicated. A solution must be attempted if synecology is to be possible. Why is this problem so difficult? We have already discovered some reasons connected with the use of a sweep net. Some insects either fly away or drop to the ground when anyone comes near, even two or three metres away. These micromigrations displace part of the fauna from the tops of the plants to their roots, while only the tops are being investigated.

At one time I tried, with several of my students, to sample this or that part of a plant with a 'sampler': a cylindrical box cut along both sides and with sharpened edges. This is brought close to the plant with great care, and then suddenly shut, cutting off and enclosing the bit of plant that one wants to study. It is later opened inside a large plastic bag which contains a killing agent, and on return to the laboratory the catch can be examined after separating it from the vegetable material. The number of insects that can be caught in this way is surprising. They differ, moreover, not only quantitatively but also qualitatively from what is caught in a sweep net or a suction trap. It may be added that the sampler allows sampling of the upper, middle or even lower parts of the plants at will.

But then, you may say, haven't you got here a neat way of getting a statistical picture of the population that is sufficiently accurate? Unfortunately this is not quite certain, because we have no standard of comparison. Old workers had an almost religious faith in the *cylinder*. This was a metal cylinder with cutting edges, which was forced into the ground to surround the plant that one wanted to study. If this was done quickly enough the entire fauna was imprisoned, and could be killed and sorted out in the laboratory. This has been mentioned already. Clearly in a reasonable world this method would be perfect, though tedious, but let us put it to the test. Very late in the day, because I myself was also influenced by the cult of the cylinder, I decided to make myself one, and then I asked two of my students to try it out on our eternal field of alfalfa. When they returned the least one could say was that they were not overcome with enthusiasm. The first part of the operation worked out just as it is described in books, but when it came to gathering up the small and even minute insects fallen down to the ground when they were killed, my two ecologists were forced to admit themselves beaten. These tiny insects were hopelessly lost among the fragments of vegetable debris.

What can we do then? The sad thing is that at the present moment we know far too little about it. That is to say we have not even a tedious method that can be relied upon. It is just as if the officials who were taking a census could never be sure that they had received all the forms relating to a particular town; or worse still, that they knew for certain that several categories of citizens were missing, without knowing exactly which.

Other methods have been devised, which have been in use for so short a time that their value cannot be guaranteed. For example, if after having stretched round the trunk of a tree a sheet of very large size, one gives the tree a big dose of insecticide, a staggering number of insects fall on to the sheet, especially if one takes care to shake the branches. Perhaps one could drench a particular area of alfalfa with a massive dose of insecticide, having first placed on the ground plastic discs to catch the bodies? All this remains to be done.

Insects moving about on the surface of the soil

Other situations require other methods. The briefest observation, in the month of June particularly, will show what a variety of insects and spiders moves about between the stems in a cultivated field. We must remember that they are living there in a world completely different from the world above. They receive almost no rain, for it is almost completely intercepted by the plants (this is especially true of alfalfa's interlacing leaves); cut off also are almost all the sun's rays, apart from the green and infra-red light.

Let us say straight away that, as we shall see in the next few chapters, the fauna is materially different from that which can be caught at the surface of the 'ocean of vegetation'. But here we have a simple and very effective method, the Barber trap, which the Germans have used intensively. This is a glass jar with a wide aperture, which contains water to which has been added formalin or some other toxic substance, and which is sunk into the soil so that insects fall into it. Williams (1958) has even combined with the Barber trap a device for timing the catch. Underneath the funnel which is the trap proper are a number of jars mounted on a rotating disc, so that they come into position in succession, at the rate, for example of one jar every hour. According to Williams this method seems to be reliable enough, although *Oribates* and Hymenoptera are well known to avoid Barber traps. According to Skuhravy (1957) the very big species are caught more successfully than the tiny ones.

The fauna of trees

Here is yet another environment where the techniques of sampling are not the same. The older workers, and even some modern ones, have used without question a venerable piece of apparatus which can already be seen in old entomological books round about 1880: an entomologist in a long smock, booted like an explorer, and wearing an artist's felt hat, holds in one hand an inverted umbrella beneath a branch, which he is striking with a stick. Down into the umbrella fall all the insects that have nothing better to do: that is, those that have no wings to fly away, or which have not clung tightly enough to the twigs. When it is realised that certain amateurs, who shall be nameless, write 'quantitative' studies on the basis of such collections, it can be seen how little progress has been made by the science of synecology. Clearly, though the 'Japanese Umbrella' may be useful to the systematic entomologist it is no good at all to students of populations and statisticians.

So we must look for something else. I have already mentioned the massive treatment of a tree with insecticide, but even then a certain number of insects may remain clinging to the bark, or in the foliage. It is preferable to do as Lepointe has done, to enclose a branch in a big plastic bag, which is closed up as soon as the branch has been cut off. In the laboratory the mass of insects is counted.

There remains one zone that has never been methodically explored, that is the bark of the trunk and branches. Along with Lepointe I have been able to carry out quantitative collecting by soaking wads of material in chloroform and applying them to the bark. The number of insects that can be collected by doing this is unbelievable.

The fauna of the soil

The soil, the fauna living in it, and the methods of collecting that fauna are enough to provide a book in themselves, and many entomologists work on nothing else. This fauna and the microfauna and microflora associated with it play an important part in breaking down plant remains and creating humus. The fuller understanding of the phenomenon of 'humidification' appears more and more to be the basic task of the agronomist.

Unfortunately the techniques of sampling soil insects run up against a number of difficulties. A very large number of small insects remain between particles of soil, and in a different way in different types of soil. In the first place attempts were made to change the texture of the soil by various treatments which, it was thought, would enable the fauna to be completely recovered by repeated washing and 'panning'. Other research workers were bent on perfecting a piece of apparatus that is almost as tricky to use as a sweep net: the Berlese funnel. One of these sacred cows is to be found in every ecological laboratory.

A giant funnel is fixed to a frame over a narrow-mouthed flask. The sample of soil to be studied is placed on a grid in the upper part of the funnel, and an electric lamp or a radiator shines on to its upper surface. All the books describe what the insects ought then to do: driven back by the heat they cannot decently do otherwise than move from the upper layers of soil, through lower and lower layers, pass the grid, and fall down the funnel into the waiting

Figure 21. MacFadyen's elaborate apparatus for extracting arthropods from the soil. A paraffin heater shown in section (1) with its flame (e) produces hot air, which follows the path of the arrows. The apparatus is circular, and hot air passes over all the funnels (f) with the soil samples (g) in tubes (j). The insects move away from the heat and dryness through the gauze (h) into the tubes (k) (see also the photograph on page 70).

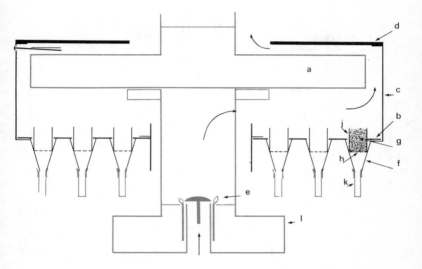

container. Nothing remains then but to count them, to describe them, and to write papers on the fauna of the soil and its variations.

What is the value of such papers? One should not be afraid to say there is almost none, at least from the quantitative point of view, which is what is most interesting to the ecologist. For when tiresome people began to look into the value of the Berlese funnel for quantitative studies, what a mess! Certain insects did not go on moving down through the soil as it was heated, but came to rest with 'heat stupor', and died on the spot. And worst of all, in a different kind of soil, or in a slightly modified Berlese funnel, or with a different way of heating it, they could escape from the soil perfectly well.

In spite of all this, MacFadyen (1953) tried to make certain improvements to the Berlese funnel. He took only small soil samples, avoided compacting them in any way, which might help to immobilise the insects; and he also placed the sample of soil on the

Figure 22. Equipment for separating small arthropods from water, soil or vegetation. **A.** Washing from soil by means of a jet of water: **a, b, f** are sieves of graded sizes; **c** is a sedimentation can, which can be tilted on a pivot **e**; **g** is a chamber from which the water passes to its final sieving through bolting silk in tube **h**. **B.** Flotation chamber in which the arthropods trapped on the sieves are floated off; a flotation solution such as magnesium sulphate is introduced through the lower tube, with

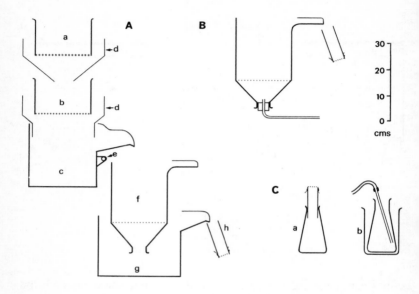

grid upside down so that what had been the surface now lay under-neath. The idea was that burrowing animals, which are normally found deep in the soil could and should work their way through the whole thickness of the soil sample; while those living at the surface, non-fossorial types, would now have only a few millimetres to go to escape from the soil. This trick of inverting the soil sample is surely most ingenious, but do the insects really behave as Mac-Fadyen hoped they would? He asserts that in any case he retrieved by this method as many individuals as by the flotation method to be described presently, but admits all the same that many Collembola cannot be recovered, nor can many mites.

Since that time a good many others have suggested improve-ments. Murphy (1958) wanted to be given only very thin layers of soil, and required that the vegetable litter lying on the ground

bubbles of air. **C.** Separation of the animals from the vegetation: in **a** the contents of the small tube **h** are tipped into a flask into which **b** benzene is then introduced gradually with stirring. The vegetation remains, but the animals float off into the outer beaker (after Salt).

should be removed as a preliminary step; if this was not done the insects were very slow to move downwards. It is true to say that each group of micro-arthropods, and every different type of soil calls for special treatment.

We might wonder then why stubborn research workers persist in trying to improve an apparatus the very principle of which is without doubt marred by serious defects. They do so for the same reason that the sweep net is still used, because the results are striking and more or less automatic. It is a very pretty sight to see twenty Berlese funnels, all in a row, endlessly 'distilling' insects into a series of flasks. And it is cruel to declare that the figures so easily obtained have no value at all. All the more so because, if you disown the Berlese funnel, what remains except the fiddling *flotation method*?

This method offers many more guarantees than Berlese's method, but to put it into operation with precision will still call for patient research work. The great problem here is to break down the texture of the soil, crumbling it into granules so fine that no arthropod can hide inside one. Salt insists that freezing to $-12°C$ is sufficient; after warming up again, the soil goes quickly and completely into suspension in water, and lends itself well to the flotations and filterings which are basic to this method and especially so if at the time of flotation benzene is added, which wets the cuticle of the arthropods, but not the vegetable debris. The former therefore pass into the layer of benzene, while the vegetable particles remain floating at the interface between the benzene and the water. If a vacuum pump is used at the same time, the bubbles of air that are keeping the particles of vegetable matter afloat are sucked out, and the particles sink to the bottom of the water. It then becomes so easy to recover the arthropods that Salt was able to extract 260,000 where by the standard methods he had extracted only some 900.

But three French workers, d'Aguilar, Benard and Bessard had a very simple thought, which seems never to have occurred to anyone before. When it is a question of how to break down the

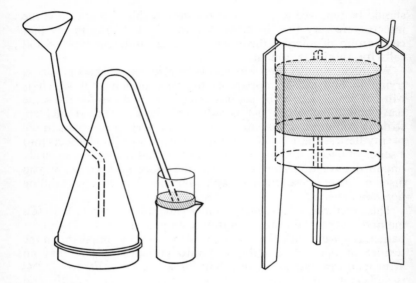

Figure 23. Separation of soil arthropods by the methods of Aguilar, Benard and Bessard: *left*, separating by density; *right*, the filter trough that is used for the early samples (see Chauvin, 1956).

structure of the soil the pundits must have some idea; why not ask them? And in fact Demolon's method has long been in use; the sample is soaked in 1 % solution of sodium citrate, when the lumps of soil break up with the greatest ease. d'Aguilar and his colleagues thereupon washed their samples of soil in a trough ending in a very fine filter, and thus extracted all particles smaller than the smallest arthropods that were being looked for. After several such filtrations through finer and finer filters the liquid was sorted in a 'separator' containing another, heavier liquid, which extracted the mineral constituents.

The significant point, which few workers had thought of, is that the method was standardised by introducing into a soil sample a number of strange arthropods, and confirming that these were always recovered.

Automatic sorting. All these methods, both those applied to the fauna of the soil and those used for the vegetation layer, involve counts of insects, exacting and inordinately long, which tie down an army of technicians. This is one of the factors which restricts, and always will restrict, the progress of ecology. Could one not at least find a way of making the counting automatic.

This is not a dream, as might be thought. If two species are separated by a host of characters, there is one of these that is not regularly made use of: their density. The bacteriologists have now reached the point of being able to separate species of bacteria by suspending them in a liquid of convenient density. Seinhorst has separated one species of Nematode from another in this way. And again, Fay & Morland (1959) automatically separated the two sexes and the different larval instars of a culture of mosquitoes. It is enough to let the culture flow between two glass plates which meet at an angle that can be varied to ensure that one litre flows through in forty-five seconds. The sexes and the various instars sort themselves out into overlapping bands which can be recovered in succession at the lower end. Lowe and Dromgoole (1956) went a stage further than this, by fitting an electronic counter to count aphids suspended in a liquid, and such a counter could easily be adapted for other insects.

Elaboration of the results – statistics again

This is a tricky aspect, and one that has developed considerably in recent years. There exist today a very large number of articles, and even entire periodicals devoted to the mathematical appreciation of variations in populations. Demography, whether human or animal, is a child of mathematics.

It is not enough to have collected the insects in a field of alfalfa for instance, throughout a period of one month. Suppose we want to discover whether the fluctuations of the population follow the fluctuations of temperature. We need to find out what variation in populations exists between days when the temperature is identical, because this is biology, and in this science no one has ever known one factor to remain constant, even when the external conditions remain the same. The next step is to find out whether the variations that come about when the temperature is varied are big enough to have a statistical significance; in other words, what degree of confidence can one place in these figures, and if they are reliable, do they show any relation to the variations of temperature?

Statistics can be applied to another method that is strangely simple, and which gives another way of assessing population fluctuations. This method was put into practice by C. H. N. Jackson, and the principle is now well known to ecologists. It is necessary first to catch a very large number of the insects concerned, several thousands, and to mark them, either by a coloured spot, or by feeding them with a radioactive isotope. Later they are released, and collecting them is continued day by day, noting the proportions of marked and unmarked insects that are taken. It is the dilution that we are trying to measure, and it is obvious that the more numerous the unmarked insects (the 'solvent') the lower will be the concentration of the marked insects (the 'solute'). By repeating these measurements at the periphery and in the middle of an infested area it is even possible to calculate indexes of immigration and emigration. Adams (1951) drew up tables which make it possible to assess the statistical significance of methods of capture and re-capture.

There have been many applications of mathematics and of statistics to ecology. Cole (1946) tried to analyse in this way the *degree of aggregation* of a population. It is found that in fact living organisms only very rarely show a random distribution, but tend to stay in groups of two, three or four: as, for example among birds. This is a kind of distribution that is called 'contagious', and the mathematical theory of it is well known. From it the degree of interattraction can be estimated.

Williams has also shown the possibility of determining an *index of diversity*, with the help of 850,000 moths that he caught at Rothamsted. According to the mathematician Fisher, if we take samples of a population at random, we ought to find a large number of species represented by one individual, half of the number of species represented by two individuals, one-third by three individuals, and so on. The expression $n_1 \; (-\log_e(1-x)/x)$ represents the total number of species where x is a constant less than unity, and n_1 the number of species of which there is only one individual. When different samples are taken from the same population n_1/x is constant, and characteristic of the population.

When on the other hand, we plot on the abscissa the number of individuals, and on the ordinate the number of species, we obtain a hyperbola, which proves clearly that the distribution of species among a series of samples obeys a simple law. According to Williams there is a linear relationship between the number of species and the logarithm of the number of individuals. In a large sample the index of diversity corresponds in practice to the number of species that are represented by a solitary individual. The measurement of the index of diversity enables one to avoid some of the mistakes that are generally made. For instance, in an environment that is unfavourable, and has a small fauna, we may find that the number of species per genus is smaller than it is in a more numerous population: but that may arise quite simply from the fact that we have taken an insignificant sample from the denser population.

The measurement of the index of diversity is therefore essential. It shows from the start some quite curious things: fewer genera are found in a small population; there exists a kind of selection which operates in favour of 'more than one species, all in the same genus', rather than 'a single species in different genera'. Tables have also been constructed from which any of three quantities (index of diversity; number of species; number of individuals) can be calculated, provided that one knows the other two (Fisher, Corbett & Williams, 1943).

Mathematical ecology, and ecology on the spot

These very brief and outrageously condensed accounts show clearly the way in which mathematicians and ecologists can and should help each other. In the interests of truth I am obliged to admit that they are very far from doing so, and that on the contrary they wouldn't think of it. The ecologists of the open air accuse the mathematicians of starting with preconceived ideas, and of misleading simplification; or arbitrarily neglecting particular factors, and of having not the least idea of the way in which these problems really present themselves in nature. And they are not mistaken, as we shall see from examples a little later. But on the other hand, do the ecologists think we can go on indefinitely ignoring statistics and population analyses, whether human or animal? That would obviously be absurd.

The evil arises, I think, because many ecologists have simply no taste for being demographers, and have no contacts with those who make studies of human populations. Thus the idea of establishing mortality tables for insects, classifying them by age-groups, is relatively recent. Watt (1961) achieved this, and entered the results on punched cards, which could be fed into a computer. The way is now open for the 'simulation' of biological processes affecting populations: by introducing, for example, a theoretical mortality factor which affects only old eggs, and then studying what the consequences would be. . . .

The main argument against mathematicians by the field ecologists is that one could not know how to understand, and above all how to express quantitatively, all the factors that enter into variations of population. But Morris and Watt have retorted (1962) that few of these factors are really important outside a few 'key characters', and there are often not more than four or five of these. Thus mathematical analysis could easily be carried out. For instance 68–90 % of the examples chosen by Watt depend on variations of a single stage, the number of eggs surviving. It can be tested whether this is really a key character by making on this basis alone forecasts about the development of the population that can be precisely verified later (see pages 89–90).

On the other hand, one factor that may disconcert the field entomologist is the fact that nature is 'non-Markovian', that is to say that the results of a strategy, such as an insecticidal treatment, cannot be expressed by a Markov series. In a series of this type changes between time t and time $t + 1$ are solely a function of the state at time t. Now in nature they may often depend on the state at $t-1$. And the analysis carried out by Watt of the fluctuations of *Bupalus piniarius* show an even closer correlation with state $t-2$ than $t-1$, this arising from the fact that certain factors show their effects only after a long delay. (A Markov series, or rather a Markovian sequence expresses the concept of events that are mutually dependent, one on another. A sequence $x_1, x_2 \ldots x_n$ forms a Markovian sequence if knowing x_1 and x_n allows us to predict with certainty x_{n+1}. Ecological events have too many ramifications to be arranged into linear Markovian sequences.)

A female of the house cricket, *Gryllulus domesticus*, an insect that is widely used in laboratory experiments because it is very easily bred. The house cricket shows a number of complex 'group-effects', which are described in the text (page 110).

3 In the laboratory

There is a schism that runs through ecology, and through biology as a whole, dividing the field worker from the laboratory man. I have already hinted at this in the previous chapters, but it is not easily understood by outsiders. It is as if they were two different kinds of intellect, diverging not so much in their conception of the problems, as in the temperament with which they tackle them.

One lot love the open air, active and prolonged exercise in the woods and forests. Direct observation of nature has convinced them quickly – too quickly – that 'indoor' theories are erratic and contradictory. In addition they themselves have little inclination for theorising and even less for devising experiments. They admit that experiment is the foundation of science, but this is lip service only, because in practice they never experiment.

I have met biologists of this type, especially when, following up my research in the laboratory, I went out to study migratory locusts in the field. I had to put up more than once with teasing about laboratory experts, but actually I didn't mind very much, because the open-air types did not know what they were talking about when they jeered at laboratory work. The majority, ninety-nine per cent of them, had never done any, properly speaking. Their experience was essentially systematic, and once they ventured away from pure taxonomy they felt lost; whence the understandable defensive reflex of making fun of what they did not understand.

At the opposite extreme are those who have never been outside the laboratory, and do not wish to go outside it. Because, they say, in the field one can never interpret a phenomenon correctly; there are too many different factors, impossible to isolate. These are the chaps who do all their work on jars of *Tribolium* or *Drosophila* to bolster up the theories of population dynamics that we shall be talking about presently. These are the same people who formerly built up the theory of tropisms, and 'behaviour under controlled conditions', until the successful campaign of Lorenz and his Viennese followers demonstrated to them that nevertheless, animals are more natural at liberty than in a cage.

An enlarged view of the house cricket, in which it can just be seen that the fore wings (tegmina) are partly opened. The cricket is *stridulating*: i.e. producing sound by rubbing the tegmina together.

Naturally, and as ever, the truth lies somewhere between these two extremes. We must try to find the difficult balance between these two attitudes of mind. It is quite true that field work only rarely leads to certainties, but it is wrong to assert that this rules out making experiments. In fact there exists, as Lepointe has clearly shown, one type of ecological experiment that can very well be carried out in the field, and which is not so difficult to interpret.

For instance, says Lepointe, you suspect that certain species hide themselves in the middle of evergreen foliage because the humidity is greater there than elsewhere. This is indicated by the similarity between the curves for the total number of captures and for the variation of humidity. Why not give the foliage a good watering? If this similarity means anything, then the number of insects should increase rapidly, and then remain high for some time, because we have learned from microclimatology that the effects of a shower persist for many hours. If the results do not conform to our forecast, then some factor other than humidity must be involved, for instance temperature. Perhaps the insects have chosen, not a high humidity, but a low temperature. Right then, why not put the plant into shade by setting up opaque screens, when the temperature will drop. It is true that the light is being cut off at the same time, and that in that case two factors are being varied together, and this is not sound experimental practice. But by using a bigger screen and placing it farther away, one can still cut off direct light while admitting more diffused light, and thus to a certain degree separate the two factors of light and heat. A little thought will soon show what a variety of experiments on these lines can be devised.

It is thus never impossible to carry out experiments; it all depends whether the would-be experimenter has imagination or not. It is not possible to do everything in the laboratory, nor yet everything in the field. Common sense therefore suggests that specialists in the two branches should help one another. They would do this if only scientists were always reasonable men, but alas . . . !

Laboratory methods of population studies

From the start, therefore, we have tried to simplify the tangled interrelations that are found under natural conditions, and to reduce them to the scale of the laboratory. Very many insects can be reared in bottles, and then it looks as if we could control the external and internal conditions under which their development takes place. Periodical censuses of the population provide a solid mathematical basis from which can be distilled, as if by magic, general laws to be applied to the insect under natural conditions. This soon has to be qualified, as we shall see. Yet many research workers find this type of work congenial, and the literature on the populations of grain-feeding insects (which are particularly popular as a subject for study) grows steadily every day. I am sure that the '*Tribolium* jar' will end up by rivalling the '*Drosophila* jar' of the geneticists.

These matters have gone so far that at the Congress of Entomology in Montreal I was able to admire a marvellous apparatus built by Stanley (1952), called an 'autotrephon'. Here jars of grain infested with *Tribolium* moved progressively along a ramp, while all the optimum conditions of temperature and humidity were maintained. At regular intervals the apparatus itself took a sample, sifted out the *Tribolium*, and separated them from their food material, so that the experimenter had only to count them. Let us hope that before long a suitable electronic device will supplant the experimenter completely, and replace him with a computer.

As I have just said, the material obtained in such ways lends itself very well to mathematical analysis, but I only mention this in passing because, I must confess, my mathematical competence, like that of most biologists, is very limited.

It seems clear that the insects that live in grain and in flour, and especially *Tribolium*, were chosen not because they were of special interest scientifically, but because they fulfilled some of the requirements of a convenient laboratory animal. It is for the same reason that experimental psychologists make white rats run round a labyrinth, without asking themselves whether the white rat in itself is any more important than any other vertebrate animal, nor even if it is specially representative of the class Mammalia. And it is very likely that the science of genetics is founded on *Drosophila* because this fly is easy to rear in bottles.

These gently ironical remarks should not be taken for serious criticisms. I myself have often been drawn to a particular line of work because it was convenient for experiment, and the most beautiful experimental scheme in the world must have one qualification above all: it must be possible to carry out in practice. We all regard ourselves as a special case, but we should be aware of this, and not draw general conclusions from our work without due care.

As far as the insects living in grain and flour are concerned, it may be asked, all the same, if such insects do not have a peculiar biology, and if this is not too far removed from that of plant-feeding insects in the wild, for instance. May not these fundamental differences be one of the reasons why field ecologists so rudely reject conclusions that seem clear to the 'Tribolium School'?

In every respect the remarkable efforts of dedicated research workers has revealed a host of facts about the biology of populations of grain-feeding insects that are certainly useful. As Pack says, even if the Tribolium jar is open to criticism, it must nonetheless be admitted that here is a *biological model*, that it is not artificial in every respect, and that the conclusions drawn from it can be applied, at the lowest reckoning, to a group of pests that is very widely distributed. There is nothing to prevent the theory being elaborated later in order to adapt it to other kinds of phenomena.

Social relations among insects

It is not long before one becomes aware that every animal reacts when another of its kind comes near, not only in behaviour, but equally by physiological changes: growth, appetite, entry into diapause, etc. . . . These are the so-called 'group effects', which have particularly interested French workers. Their centre of interest is thus far removed from that of American workers, who rear very large populations of grain insects, and apply statistics to them; their approach is typically demographic. But the Americans never ask themselves, for example, whether the biology of two Tribolium together differs in any respect from that of an isolated individual.

Now this is what the French workers study, those who are in this field: physiological interaction between individuals of the same species, present in small numbers. They have studied such group effects in a wide variety of insects: grasshoppers, cockroaches, crickets, aphids, caterpillars, processionary and others, bees, ants, wasps, stick insects, etc. From all this emerges a range of complex mutual reactions, quite different from the soft pillow of simple, mechanical factors upon which certain research workers take it easy.

Very often individuals of the same species stimulate each other to grow much more quickly. Such a reaction is sensorial in origin, and often can be suppressed or reversed by cutting off the appropriate sense-organs. I insist on the fact that the acceleration of growth (or the prolongation of survival in the case of social insects) is very important, and should quite do away with the attraction of those curves of population growth, above all in the early stages. Quite soon, moreover, when the density of population becomes too great, there appear semi-pathological phenomena of overpopulation, overcrowding, and then the rate of growth becomes greatly retarded and disturbed. It is precisely with this second phase that the American school is especially concerned, whereas the French school is exclusively concerned with the former.

The mathematical approach

Finally, as we have already said, there is another method of tackling the problem, in the laboratory as well as in the field; the mathematical approach. This seems to offer a better chance of success, and many biomathematicians have followed this promising line. The classical works of Verhulst, Ross, Pearle and Reed, Lotka and Volterra have demonstrated it so well that there is no need for me to enlarge on it; besides, there is enough here for another book. The biomathematicians adopt a method which is not completely absurd, and which consists of making *a priori* assertions, without asking themselves, as a preliminary, whether or not they agree with reality; these enable them to derive functions which are then, at this stage, compared with genuine population data. Here is obviously a tempting technique, which, as Neyman, Park & Scott have commented, recalls the methods used in genetics by Galton and Pearson. It can be fairly said that the bio-mathematicians have studied above all the competition between a species and its parasite.

Interactions and group effects in a homogeneous population (i.e. with one species only)

American work on *Tribolium* and *Tenebrio* is so extensive that it is impossible to give a full account of it here, and I must be satisfied to emphasise a few points. For example, Leslie and Park (1949) wanted to apply to *Tribolium* the same formulae that are used to calculate the *intrinsic natural growth rate* of man. The life table, or *lx* function, giving the probability at birth of a female being alive at age x gives us the force of mortality $\mu_x = -dl_x/l_x \cdot dx$. ... It can be shown, however (e.g. Lotka 1922–6; Leslie 1945), that a population will increase in numbers N at a rate $dN/dt = rN$ where the parameter r is termed that natural rate of increase ... It is to be noted that the intrinsic rate $r = b - d$, the difference between the birth-rate and the death-rate per head in a population with a stable age distribution.

For *Tribolium*, Leslie and Park shows that $r = 0.105$ per day; this means that a population increasing at this rate doubles itself in six to nine days, or grows 10.5% per day. Births are 0.154 per day per head, and deaths 0.053.

Various authors, such as Watt (1955) and Utida (1956) have made use of another method, which is most interesting because it is an example of very precise experimental demography. One would imagine that no one has understood the importance of this research, because it has not had, in my opinion, the response that it deserves. Like all the best ideas, the one from which Watt and Utida started off is very simple. You assume that rates of birth and of death follow such and such a curve, which you have decided upon in advance. *Then what is to stop you from subtracting* – or conversely adding – *one age-group* (eggs, larvae, pupae, perfect insects) and then analysing the consequences of doing this? Do they or do they not conform to the calculations that you have carried out in advance?

Watt started off from a mathematical study of the possibilities of exploiting fisheries; it is obviously very important to know what average quantity of fish can be withdrawn without the risk of compromising the natural powers of recuperation of the population. Many other biomathematicians are brooding over this problem, which bristles with difficulties. Now the possibility of recouping losses depends not so much on the total number of individuals remaining as upon their age-distribution. *Productivity may even increase up to a certain level of exploitation*, between certain obvious limits; a well regulated fishery reduces intraspecific competition by eliminating, for example, adults too old to breed. Moreover, the population exhibits a certain homeostasis, in the sense that the replacement individuals tend towards the same age as those abstracted; that is to say that at the end of a certain time the age-pyramid appropriate to the species and to the environment tends to be restored.

When the rate of fishing is moderate, the oscillations of population die out, because the mechanism of oscillation depends to a large extent on the accumulation of old adults, and these are not forthcoming. The important point is that the conclusions are very much the same whether they refer to fishes or to *Tribolium*. But it is necessary to guard against thinking that everything is clear, because a large part of the variations of the population is neither understood nor predictable. One of the later phases of Watt's work is quite misleading in this respect. Using a mathematical model with thirty-nine parameters (!), he says, there still remain 34% of the variations which have not been taken into account. Must we then throw up the sponge and give up trying to analyse the results of using insecticide on a field? Certainly not, as we shall see; but let us quote again from the work of Utida, who withdrew from cultures of *Calandra oryzae* all the adults after five, ten, fifteen, twenty and twenty-five days. Then there could be seen the continuous variations of the curve of reproduction (relation between density of offspring and density of parents); and the curve of the population of *Calandra*, normally very different from that of *Tribolium*, approaches it more closely as the adults are left in the medium for a shorter and shorter time.

Latest developments of mathematical demography in insects

Watt did not stop at the somewhat disillusioning remark that I quoted above. He continued to try to apply to insects the techniques of human demography, and to that end he entered the diverse characteristics of a population on to punched cards: distribution of larval stages, expectation of life of each stage, etc. (1961). This kind of detailed documentation of demographic data finds more and more use and interest among ecologists and Keizo Kiritani (1962) drew up for *Nezara viridula* very detailed tables giving information about the expectation of life at each stage. Once all these data have been coded into perforations on cards, they can be fed into a computer, and thus carry out the kind of experiment that will promote rapid progress in experimental psychology: the simulation by a machine of a biological process.

Watt used this technique to calculate the probable effect of an insecticidal treatment. The machine showed clearly one fact that the experimenters were hardly expecting: many of the treatments were incapable of reducing the population below 35%, or even below 57%. *Watt admitted voluntarily that the toxic chemicals reduced intraspecific pressure to a point at which an enormous compensatory growth of population could not fail to appear as a direct result.*

On the same occasion, and still with the help of calculating machines and methods of simulation, Morris and Watt (1963) gave a very interesting reply to the eternal objection of field ecologists:

that they know that the biomathematicians are giving themselves a lot of trouble for nothing because we cannot understand, and even more express numerically, all the factors that are in operation to cause the variations of the population. In actual fact, say Morris and Watt, outside a few 'key factors', there are hardly any which really matter; and often not more than four or five of such factors can be found.

Among five insect pests that Watt took as examples, 68–90 % of the variation depended on variations in a single stage, the number of eggs effectively laid. More important, this idea of key factors was submitted by these two authors to the iron rule of science, that is testing by experiment, and by making predictions; and they were able to make in this way sufficiently accurate forecasts about the development of the population of the pests being studied.

Effect of various environmental factors

The temperature at which insects are reared is clearly an important factor, but we have seen that the mere presence of the insects themselves alters the temperature, and may therefore act as an obstacle to their development. Humidity, if it goes beyond a certain level, militates against the growth of populations of *Tribolium*, as a result of the development of a fungus. But when these phenomena are studied in detail everything becomes more complex. In practice a distinction must be drawn between the humidity of the air and that of the flour, which are not directly linked together; or more precisely, the humidity of the superficial layers of the flour is controlled more closely by that of the surrounding air than is the humidity of the deeper layers. According to the time of day, and according to the size of the population, micro-migrations take place from the upper layers to the lower. For another thing, the different stages react differently to humidity. . . .

Above all, in considering the environmental factors, *conditioning* must not be forgotten: i.e. the accumulation in the flour of excrements and other secretions of the insects themselves, which gradually change the nature of the breeding medium. This factor has been studied with very great care, and details can be found in the great work on ecology by Allee, Park, Emerson & Schmidt. Flour thus 'conditioned' has curious and varied effects, sometimes unexpected. For example the fecundity of the insects is diminished, not surprisingly because the *Tribolium* are drugged to some extent. But there is also a diminution of egg-eating, though by what means is unknown. Now according to the Americans, this tendency of insects to eat the eggs that have just been laid is one of the most powerful factors in keeping down the population – though we shall see a little later on that these ideas have recently been greatly modified.

Females reared on new flour, mated with males reared on conditioned flour, lay few eggs. This shows how complicated must be the mechanism by which fecundity is reduced, since it works on the males as well as on the females. The older authors, nevertheless, do not seem to have been able to find out the fertility of the eggs, that is to say the percentage capable of hatching, but that is because they did not look closely enough to see clearly, as we do.

A landmark of animal demography: the work of Le Gay Brereton

Amongst the mass of published work that a scientist is forced to go through if he wishes to be in the swim, it is not a common experience to come upon a piece of work that drags you out of the blessed state of the 'library doze'; by which I mean that task of taking notes of other people's work, and deciding at what point they become wearisome, and without inspiration; that is one's daily bread. How many bulky memoirs can be adequately summarised in a few lines! And how very much rarer are those, much slimmer, perhaps, in the number of their pages, which bring you sharply out of your slumbers. The note of Le Gay Brereton is one of those, but in order to appreciate its importance we must make a detour by way of the researches of Christian and his school on mice.

Christian noted certain very strange anomalies in the reproduction of mice reared in a terrarium. For a given area, if they were not interfered with, and on condition, of course, that the food was unlimited, there were always the same number of mice after the same interval of several months. In the same period their suprarenal glands underwent characteristic changes. These were of normal size at the beginning, when the population was still relatively sparse, but they soon began to enlarge, in step with the increasing numbers of mice. Eventually the suprarenals were very big, and at the same time the reproduction of the mice ceased almost completely. It was not that the males ceased to mate with the females, but the latter did not conceive any young, an effect that is certainly related to the disturbance of the suprarenals and hypophyses. If one now gave the mice access to another terrarium, their density in the original cage fell, and at once the suprarenals regained their original size, and reproduction returned to normal.

Influenced by these very odd results, Le Gay Brereton had the idea of studying the fertility of the eggs of *Tribolium* in much more detail than had been done hitherto. It is enough for this purpose to sieve the flour regularly and remove the eggs straight after egg-laying so as almost completely to avoid egg-eating. Now the more numerous the population with which one has infested a given amount of flour, the smaller the percentage of eggs that will hatch. There must therefore be some way in which the females control the fertility of the eggs above and beyond any other regulating mechanism, and in relation to the size of the population.

This is of first importance because we are dealing with 1 a mechanism that seems to occur very widely, since it operates at one moment in mice and at another in an insect, although certainly on very different principles, since the insects have neither suprarenal glands nor hypophyses. 2 On the other hand this is a *non-Darwinian regulating system*, or one at any rate not foreseen by Darwin. There is no question here of either selection or of a struggle for existence. Long before these factors can come into play, *Tribolium* and mice can regulate their fecundity by themselves.

Now this is only one example. How many more such techniques may exist by which living systems reach a biological equilibrium? We shall see other examples in relation to group behaviour.

Other developmental factors arising from the population itself

Research workers have known for a long time that there is an optimum density for starting a culture. Chapman and Allee proved, for example, that starting off with 0·125 *Tribolium* per gram growth was more rapid than with 0·062 or higher densities. Park (1932–3) confirmed this. MacLayen put 8·8·8·4·8·16 pairs of *Tribolium* in 16·8·4·1·1·1 grams of flour, and according to him the optimum was found to be two weevils per gram.

Crombie (1942) however, starting off with fertilised females, no longer found that the density of the initial culture affected the rate of growth of the population.

Again according to Crombie (1942) crowding of the adult insects invariably reduced the rate of egg-laying of most grain-feeding insects, but fertility was not affected – directly contrary to the findings of Le Gay Brereton, no doubt because the experimental conditions were different. Crombie thought that the disturbing factor was competition for egg-laying sites; there is certainly some truth in this, since Ito noted that the number of pits that *Tribolium* digs in the flour as a preliminary to egg-laying is directly proportional to the area of surface.

In an Oriental bruchid beetle, *Callosobruchus sinensis*, the maximum rate of development is obtained for a particular density of population, which may be considered to be the optimum, since the duration of development is also shortest at that density; nevertheless the *weight* of both male and female individuals is then at a minimum. At higher densities the number of offspring falls in inverse ratio to the density, so much so that it brings about compensating oscillations. Here the higher densities militate against both fertility and fecundity; the mortality in the pupa is also increased;

in contrast the conditioning of the breeding medium should have little effect, because the bruchids are reared on haricot beans, which become soiled less easily than flour.

In *Drosophila melanogaster* the presence of living larvae in the substratum reduces fecundity, and then the eggs are often laid, not in the nutritive medium, but on the sides of the rearing jar. The presence of old larvae in large numbers is also harmful to the viability of the eggs, which are thrown out by the larvae, and dry up. The maximum fecundity of the adults is achieved when the larval density lies between that which gives rise to the highest number of emergences of adult beetles, and that which produces the biggest adult individuals. (Chiang & Hodgson, 1950).

In *Culex pipiens autogenicus* (Ulmann, 1941) cultures that have declined and cultures that are overcrowded show the same phenomena: retardation of egg-laying, diminution in number of eggs laid. An overcrowded population keeps going thanks to a high mortality, which specially affects young larvae; hence though the number of adults remains steady, the number of larvae may undergo important fluctuations.

Group effects

As we have already seen the term 'group effect' (Grassé and Chauvin) is applied to the effects produced by proximity upon the individuals in populations of low density. Compared with an isolated individual there is usually an acceleration of development. Group effects often become detectable from two individuals onwards, provided they are crowded into a sufficiently small space. This 'criterion of two' is even one of the best tests for group effects. If no effect can be seen when two individuals are put together, then there is little hope of finding group effects whatever the density. Remember the effect of overcrowding on the mass of the individuals, and which is great enough to count as a pathological effect. But it is obvious that there are many intermediate stages between the two types of effects.

The ultimate in group effects is the *Phase Theory* of locusts, originated by Uvarov (1921). This savant seems to have been intimidated by his theory, and not to have seen all its general applications. He first noticed the transformation that took place in *Locusta danica*, where the solitary, sluggish, green hoppers changed into active insects, with variegated pattern in orange and black. This transformation is brought about by crowding, and is a reversible phase change. The gregarious phase did not differ from *Locusta migratoria*, which up to the time of Uvarov's discovery had been regarded as a different species.

The phenomenon of phases has been recognised in all the important migratory species of grasshoppers. In minor migrants, such as *Zonocerus*, which do not produce very striking swarms, the group effect is also trifling. It is possible that there, too, more intensive research would uncover all stages of transition. Later on Matthee (1945) discovered phases in the butterflies *Laphygma exempta* and *Spodoptera abyssinica;* Dould (1953) in a New Zealand Agrotid, *Persetania ervingi;* Goodwin (1953) in *Plusia gamma*; Long (1953) in all kinds of noctuid moths and even in the great Emperor Moths; Utida (1956) in the Bruchid beetle *Callosobruchus maculatus*. The development of wings in Psocids under the influence of crowding, briefly described by Badonnel (1948) also has many features of a phase-phenomenon. 'Phases' seem sufficiently widespread for us to be justified in supposing that they ought to be a quite general phenomenon.

While this is not the whole story, group effects in the limited sense may be distinguished from phase changes as follows: 1 Group effects comprise all those cases where only the rate of growth is affected by crowding, though often this effect is considerable. 2 Phase changes comprise all those cases where not only growth rate, but also structure, pigmentation, and various items of behaviour, such as activity, are modified by the crowding.

Of course this distinction is hardly more than an artificial classification, since, as I have stressed earlier several times, many intermediate stages are possible.

The desert locust, *Schistocerca gregaria*, as a fully developed, winged adult. This is the locust of the Bible, and its devastating swarms still appear throughout North Africa and the Near East.

The desert locust, *Schistocerca gregaria*, in its 'gregarious phase'. These are the five nymphal instars, or 'hoppers', with incompletely developed wings, and without the powers of flight. In the 'solitary phase' the general colour is pale green and the black spots are few or none.

Phase phenomena among migratory locusts

Migratory locusts are those huge grasshoppers, as long and thick as a finger, which belong to the genera *Schistocerca*, *Locusta*, *Nomadacris*, and which are responsible for the devastating occurrence of locust swarms. In *Locusta* and *Schistocerca* – which have been particularly studied because of their many and variable pigments, which are now well known from a chemical point of view – the 'solitary' hoppers (reared in complete isolation) are green, while the gregarious hoppers show various combinations of black, yellow and red. In the adults the colour differences are less accentuated, though sexually mature males develop a characteristic lemon yellow colour especially in *Schistocerca*.

The proportions of the body, or morphological relationships, change greatly, especially the length of the hind legs and wings, and the shape of the pronotum, the first segment of the thorax.

The two phases differ in activity, the gregarious being the more vigorous. Reproduction is also modified by phase-change. Solitary phase *Locusta* has a diapause, less pronounced in solitary *Schistocerca*. But above all, the ovarioles or egg-producing cells of the solitary individuals are more numerous than those of the gregarious ones; crowding together brings about a marked and progressive reduction in the number of ovarioles (Albrecht). This fact throws light on the appearance and disappearance of locust swarms. I have expressed certain doubts (Chauvin, 1956) about the process of multiplication in those areas where solitary locusts survive indefinitely (though very sparsely), and which correspond to only a small part of the invasion area, that is the area which the gregarious locusts frequent, but where they cannot maintain themselves.

Some people claim, with a superb assurance, to explain it all with the aid of a few simple laws derived from geometrical progressions. My objection to this is that other grasshoppers, nonmigratory, which frequent the same breeding areas as *Locusta* and *Schistocerca*, react equally favourably to better climatic conditions,

but without bursting out into enormous bands of hoppers as the migratory species do. Now Albrecht (1957) showed that individuals in the solitary phase, thanks to their large number of ovarioles, and to their increased powers of reproduction, are like a boiler under pressure, with its steam trying to burst out; and as soon as external conditions allow, the valves open, and the species reaches its maximum rate of reproduction with a rush.

The consequent crowding facilitates phase change and change of colour; and the more the insects mass together, the more their fecundity, linked to the number of ovarioles, declines. This factor, combined with the action of parasites, is sufficient explanation of their disappearance in the invasion area, where we have already noted that they appear to be unable to maintain themselves.

The importance of Albrecht's work cannot be exaggerated. It leads us to adopt a point of view about the respective fecundities of the two phases that is exactly contrary to that generally accepted by acridiologists for many years. I myself had noted (Chauvin, 1941) that the solitary individual developed more slowly than the gregarious. Albrecht added that the solitaries, and even the newly-born gregarious hoppers from parents that were grouped together, but not very densely, were slimmer at birth, and showed a tendency to undergo an extra moult, and to have biometrical characteristics proper to the solitary phase. And this, in spite of the fact that they themselves were reared in a group. So much so that it became possible to distinguish a *congregans* (that is a young locust in the process of changing from solitary to gregarious phase) from a *dissocians* (one that was changing the other way). It was this distinction that had been looked for in vain ever since Uvarov first discovered phases.

This effect of heredity comes out also in colour, and I had noticed that it is not possible to rear a high proportion of green, solitary *Schistocerca* from parents that were in the fully gregarious phase, even under the most rigorous isolation: this required isolation for at least two generations.

Obviously aggregation in nature assumes some sort of *inter-*

Figure 24. Effects of crowding on the rate of increase in weight of *Schistocerca gregaria*: when they are crowded together, males of either the solitary or gregarious phase gain weight more quickly than isolated specimens of females in gregarious phase, or males in solitary phase (Chauvin, 1941).

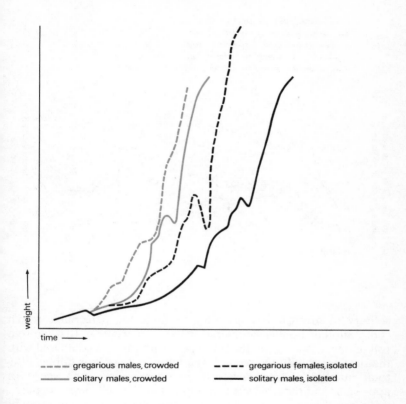

```
------ gregarious males, crowded        ---- gregarious females, isolated
------ solitary males, crowded          ──── solitary males, isolated
```

attraction, which is not easy to demonstrate; I have tried, without success. But Ellis and Pearce (1962) achieved it by offering fourth instar larvae of *Schistocerca* a choice between others of the same kind, or rolls of paper of equal size. The authors counted the numbers that approached one or the other, how long they spent close to their choice, and what their reactions were. A certain number of these reactions were the same whether the hopper was of

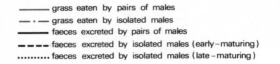

Figure 25. Group effects can be detected even when only two locusts are confined together. Males kept in pairs eat and excrete more than males kept in isolation (after Ellis).

———— grass eaten by pairs of males
— · — grass eaten by isolated males
——— faeces excreted by pairs of males
— — — faeces excreted by isolated males (early–maturing)
·········· faeces excreted by isolated males (late–maturing)

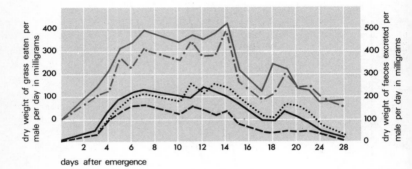

solitary or gregarious phase: for example the percentage which chose another hopper compared with the percentage that chose a roll of paper, and again, the time spent with the first compared with the time spent with the second. But among gregarious hoppers the total number of approaches to another hopper, the speed of approach, and the time spent in marching were all three greater.

As for the mechanism by which the phase change is brought about, this starts with a sensory impression. I showed in 1941 that the young migratory locusts (*Schistocerca gregaria*) isolated inside a glass sleeve, in the middle of a gregarious band, acquired the gregarious colour-pattern, which did not happen in the dark. On the other hand, a group of young solitaries kept together in complete darkness became gregarious, thus showing that some other stimulus could take the place of the visual one. I considered tactile

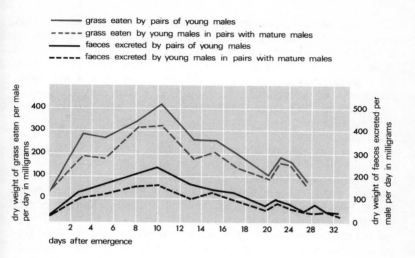

Figure 26. More group effects among pairs of locusts. Young males kept with another young male both eat and excrete more than young males kept with an older, mature male (after Ellis).

grass eaten by pairs of young males
grass eaten by young males in pairs with mature males
faeces excreted by pairs of young males
faeces excreted by young males in pairs with mature males

dry weight of grass eaten per male per day in milligrams

400
300
200
100
0

dry weight of faeces excreted per male per day in milligrams

500
400
300
200
100
0

2   4   6   8   10   12   14   16   18   20   24   28   32
days after emergence

stimuli, but it seems clear, from the work of Norris (1954) and above all of Loher (1962), about which we shall be talking shortly, that chemical stimuli must be involved as well; more precisely, the *chemoreception of contact*, to use Dethier's term. That is to say that the stimuli, to be effective, must be supplied at close proximity to the sense organs. The peculiar smell of grasshoppers, which is known to everyone who studies them, is not the olfactory stimulus that causes phase change. In fact solitaries can be reared in little cages placed side by side in the same incubator, which is pervaded with the smell of grasshopper.

It is also apparent, following the work of Joly, that special endocrine glands, the *corpora allata*, situated in insects behind the cervical ganglion, are implicated in phase-change. Grafting several pairs of these organs into a gregarious locust makes it veer towards the solitary phase. It may be, then, that the stimuli received from the other locusts inhibits the secretion from the corpora allata. On the other hand, the blood of gregarious locusts contains some factor, probably a steroid, which when injected can produce gregarious colouring in a solitary individual. There exist, therefore, two antagonistic hormones, as is generally the case in all organisms. Nickerson (1953) thinks that of these two hormones the first (the steroid) mainly affects the pattern, while the second (the 'solitary hormone') affects principally the ground colour.

This science of acridiology has recently developed along new lines which I did not suspect at the time (long ago) when I wrote my thesis on locusts. The latter dealt chiefly with what one group of research workers were interested in, and had pursued for some years. Now one point was particularly obscure: changes in gregarious pattern that could occur in *adult locusts*, and which affected the pigmentation (for example the lemon yellow colour of the gregarious male) and a number of other physiological characteristics. In the migratory locust (*Schistocerca gregaria*), the sexual maturity of the male indicated by the famous yellow tint, is speeded up by crowding together with other males of the same age or older; whereas this is not so if they are crowded together with younger males, or with females.

Now the grouping of two individuals is enough to start off the changes, even in a living space of nine litres. At first the crowded males eat and excrete more than those still isolated; but after the second and third week of crowding, feeding slows down, and then the crowded males eat less than the isolated ones.

The effect of crowding on the activity of males of *Schistocerca* is complex; crowded groups are more active than isolated individuals, but the greater part of their extra activity is expressed not in locomotion, but in the movements provoked by contacts with the others. Isolated males walk less, but jump more than those in groups. Moreover activity increases as they mature, and more quickly among isolated individuals. There is hardly any difference between the activity of young isolated males and that of groups of

The onset of the final moult of a desert locust. Soon the thorax will split along the dorsal line and the adult locust will begin to emerge.

A desert locust has just
made its final moult.
The adult insect is
still detaching itself
from the skin of the
previous instar.

two; but if a young one is placed with an older one, the young one becomes more active more quickly, and eats less, than the isolated control. But – and this is a very interesting phenomenon – *young males* have an inhibitory effect, not only on the activity, but also on the maturation, of·other young males.

Now according to Loher (1960), all these phenomena involve a *pherormone* which may be compared with that found in bees, and to understand clearly the work of Loher we must make a short digression into the ways of bees.

One of the greatest surprises of my life struck me on the day that Mlle Pain, in my laboratory, discovered that a dead queen bee, even one that had been kept for years in an insect collection, still exerts a great power over living bees. These are strongly drawn towards the corpse, which they lick, and as a consequence their ovaries shrink, and they stop making queen cells, if they had begun to do so. An alcoholic extract of the dead queen produces all these effects just as well as the queen herself, which indicates that the action is chemical in nature. Moreover, all except one of the active substances have been isolated. In the aggregate they are known as *pherormones*, from the Greek *pherein*, to carry, because these are hormones that are in a sense carried outside the body and sampled by the other individuals.

Now it is exactly this that Loher observed! He took as criterion the development of yellow colour in young males, when they are in contact, not with other young males, but with males that are already yellow. The chemical which accelerates the change is easily extracted from the bodies of yellow males by grease-solvents. A lipid extract from a yellow male, spread on a fragment of paper, and offered to a young male, is enough to initiate the colour change, but the paper must be very close, or even touching, because it does not attract males from a distance.

The antennae are the means by which this special sensitivity operates. Morris claimed that cutting off the antennae accelerates the development of the yellow pigment by shock effect, but this seems contrary to what has just been said about the rôle of the

antennae. On the other hand, I have very often cut off antennae from young males in a crowd, and I have verified the precise opposite, that this operation greatly retards the appearance of the yellow colour, or even inhibits it completely.

Among other Orthoptera, such as the long-horned grasshoppers (Tettigoniidae) gregarious changes in pigmentation, previously reported by earlier authors in the genera *Barbitistes* and *Orphania*, have been equally detected by Verdier in *Ephippigerus*. All this gives the impression that this phenomenon should be much more widespread in Tettigoniidae than had been thought. According to Key (1957) it has even been found in phasmids. In Australia the phasmids *Podacanthus wilkinsoni* and *Didymaria violaceus* damage crops, and break out into massive swarms, in the presence of which the biologist must always suspect some gregarious effect. In fact these phasmids are green in the solitary state, black and yellow when gregarious. They do not always show the concomitant differences of activity and of migration. The stimuli that come into play seem to be essentially visual; at any rate phasmids when separated by a simple metal barrier lose their solitary pigmentation.

It is the same Key who, underlining the imperfections and obscurities of the Phase Theory, in a work that caused a certain amount of stir, declared, or as good as declared, that this theory was useless for field acridiologists, who want to understand the migrations of grasshoppers, and to control them. This eternal bitter squabbling between the field and the laboratory, that I have mentioned before! Must one keep on repeating the same answer? Obviously the Phase Theory does not resolve *all* the problems of the acridiologist: who said it did? But it helps us to understand one very important point in the biology of grasshoppers, which the field biologists had never found out. There remain many other factors, as important as the Phase Theory, or even more so . . . ? Of course! Very well, let the acridiologists discover them and then study them – which they will hardly be able to do, at least in sufficient detail, except in the laboratory. . . .

This close-up view of the head of a migratory
locust, *Locusta migratoria*, shows its
formidable mouthparts. The speed with which
these can devour vegetation, together with
the great numbers of locusts present in a
swarm, make the locust a formidable enemy.

Group effects among crickets

In the course of experiments which were spread over fourteen years, I was able to bring to light a very special group effect in the domestic cricket, *Gryllulus domesticus*. When two or three young crickets, all hatched from the egg on the same day, are put together into a test tube, they do not show any striking differences from those kept isolated. A chance observation showed that only the offspring of old females (that is to say females that had been kept for a month at 30°C after their final moult) had a heredity that was susceptible to group effects. Nothing comparable could be detected in the offspring of young parents; where the parents had been of intermediate age the results were inconclusive.

Only the age of the *females* mattered. Young females mated with old males gave offspring that did not show group effects; whereas old females mated with young males gave offspring that did. Among the young offspring the stimuli that induce the group effect (more rapid increase in weight than is found in solitary crickets) are received through the cerci and the antennae. Cutting off these organs suppresses the effect, and then the crickets that are grouped together show no difference from those kept isolated.

In 1960 Fuzeau-Braesch had the good fortune to discover another group effect in a black field cricket, *Gryllus bimaculatus*, which exists in several patterns resulting from black and brown pigments. Now crickets kept in a group, even though it might be a group of only two, became paler than those crickets that were kept alone. This is quite unusual, as Fuzeau-Braesch justly remarked; in the many cases of colour changes brought about by crowding together, it is usually the individuals in a group that are dark, and the isolated ones pale. The change of pattern in *Gryllus bimaculatus* is brought about by alterations in the relative proportions of the two pigments, black and brown. This proportion is in any case very variable, with a combination of hereditary and phenotypical effects. One can also select strains of crickets that are paler or darker than the average, but this genetic control of pigmentation

Figure 27. Types of pigmentation
seen in nymphs and adults of
Gryllus bimaculatus (after Fuzeau-Braesch).

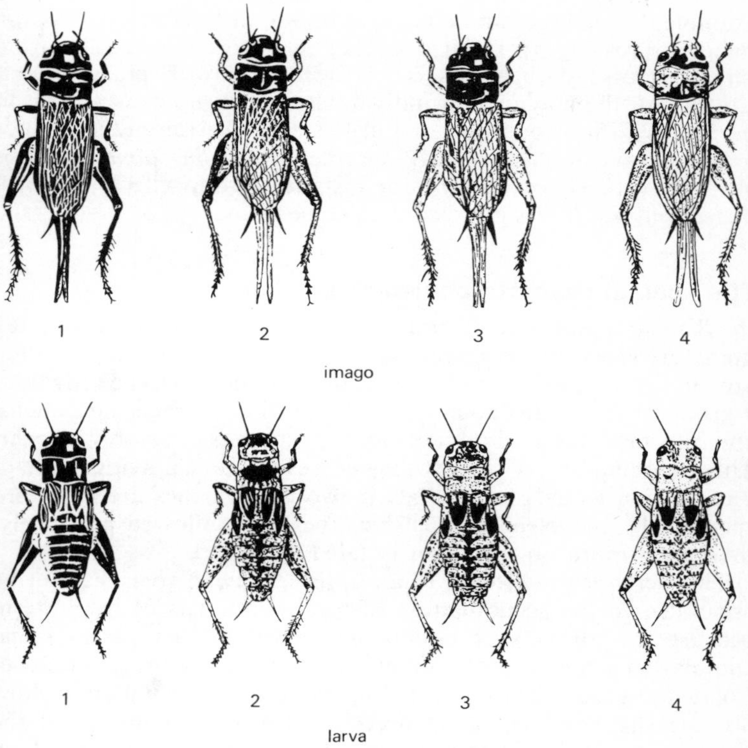

imago

larva

is polyfactorial, that is it is derived from a combination of genes.
According to Levita the production of pale individuals by a
group effect requires stimuli that are predominantly tactile, but
also includes some that are visual, olfactory and vibratory. For

example this change can be brought about, at least up to a certain point, by rearing an isolated cricket in a cage constructed from three mirrors; though this is not successful with grasshoppers. Cutting off the antennae of individuals in a group causes them to darken as if they were solitary. Furthermore the stimuli that induce group effects are not strictly specific: if *Gryllus bimaculatus* is grouped with *G. campestris*, for instance, group effects are produced, but not if it is grouped with *G. posticus*.

The special case of cockroaches

In *Blatella germanica* (Chauvin, 1946) the growth of isolated immature specimens is slightly more rapid than if two, three or ten are put together in tubes of 35 cc volume. In contrast the growth of a group of *five* is distinctly quicker than that of single specimens, and the final moult into the adult takes place notably sooner. This optimum degree of crowding corresponds to a living space of 7 cc per individual; and in fact if two cockroaches are kept in a space of 14 cc instead of the 35 cc they were allowed previously, they grow more quickly than isolated specimens.

This very clear existence of an optimum living space cannot be attributed to the accumulation of the by-products of respiration, because the air is kept circulating. On the other hand, visual stimulation is not as important as it is in crickets, since cockroaches isolated in glass tubes in the middle of a crowded population show not the slightest sign of an accelerated growth. Cutting off the antennae reduces the rate of growth of cockroaches in groups of ten down to something like that of a single individual; therefore the group effect operates through the antennae.

Yet the 'conditioning' of the food material plays some part. If the excreta of cockroaches, dried at 100°C and pulverised, are added in varying proportions, this is found to increase the growth rate in the culture, when the proportion added ranges from 1% to 5%. The chief accelerating substance is soluble in ether, thermostable, and changes slowly in the air and when exposed to light. The

Figure 28. Effects of crowding on development of colour in *Prodenia litura*. When reared under solitary conditions, approximately 24% are pale yellow-green (1), 24% pale grey (2) and 52% reddish grey; none are black. When reared under crowded conditions, about 25% are pale grey (2), 75% black (4) and none are either pale yellow-green or reddish grey.

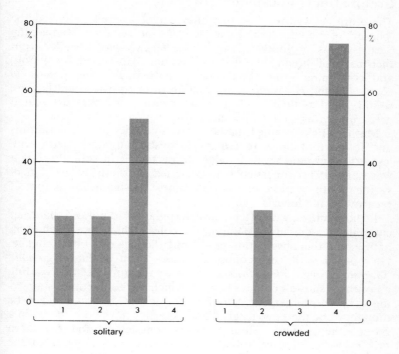

excreta of *Blabera* and *Periplaneta* mixed with the food of *Blatella* have no effect on the rate of growth. Under normal conditions the food-material of insects in a group-culture is more heavily soiled by excreta than that of isolated individuals, and their development should therefore be more rapid; but the exact opposite occurs. Doubtless the inhibitory effect of stimulation through the antennae outweighs the accelerating effect of the accumulating excreta.

Group effects in Lepidoptera

These are so well-marked that they might as well be called the 'phases' of Lepidoptera. Faure (1943), for instance, studied the 'army worms' of South Africa (*Laphygma exempta*) so-called from their habit of moving about in long columns, in perfect formation, and containing some thousands of individuals. The *Laphygma* (*L. exigua* and *L. exempta*) are dull green or brown when they are solitary, and assume a velvety black colour when they are reared gregariously, as well as also acquiring a migratory tendency.

Mathee (1945) studied the larvae of a number of noctuid moths and found that those reared gregariously had more lactic acid, less uric acid, and more fat than those reared in solitude. But it was Long (1953) in particular who carried out on the caterpillars of various moths a piece of research almost as significant as that of Uvarov on the locusts.

Lepidopterists, who often rear caterpillars, had noticed that their caterpillars were always darker in colour than those found in nature, and this observation gave Long the idea of a phase change. He worked with very common species, such as *Plusia gamma*, *Saturnia pavonia*, *Pieris brassicae*. Under the influence of crowding all of them showed colour changes, which were sometimes staggering. The caterpillars of *Saturnia*, for instance, would never be thought to be the same caterpillars after they have been reared in a group; the ground colour changes completely, and the larva bristles with coloured tubercles. It differs completely from the normal caterpillar of the Emperor Moth, though that is spectacular enough in itself. The group-effect operates only on the first stage larvae, but it remains latent, and does not become apparent until later.

The development of *Saturnia* is speeded up by crowding, the number of moults is reduced, larval mortality is less. The gregarious larvae contain more fat and less water than the solitary ones; they are more active and eat much more. The sense of vision is not involved in this phenomenon, which happens just the same in

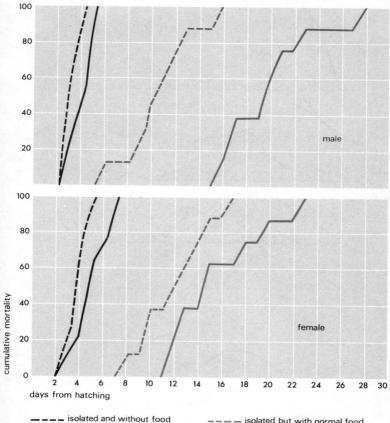

Figure 29. Whether they are kept with or without food, both males and females of *Leucania separata* survive longer if they are crowded together than if they are reared in isolation (after Iwao, 1962).

---- isolated and without food
—— crowded and without food

---- isolated but with normal food
—— crowded and with normal food

Figure 30. Effect of density of crowding on length of larval life of *Naranga aenescens*. The vertical scale shows the relative frequency of a larval life of the length indicated on the horizontal scale. The figures on the right (1, 2, 5, 10, 20) are the relative densities of individuals (after Iwao, 1962).

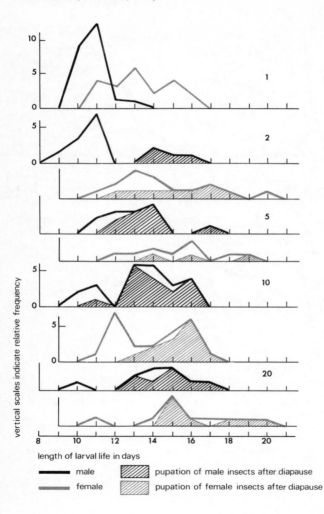

vertical scales indicate relative frequency

length of larval life in days

— male

— female

pupation of male insects after diapause

pupation of female insects after diapause

darkness. A caterpillar isolated in a transparent sleeve, but placed in the middle of a group of other larvae, remains in solitary colouring; but its colour darkens if it is kept out of sight of the others – in a sleeve of muslin, for instance – while at the same time allowing it to be aware of them, and even to make contact with them.

The study of phase changes in Lepidoptera has been carried further in recent years by the Japanese school, which has found such effects in several 'army worms' of that part of the world, which belong to the genus *Leucania*. In this genus the caterpillars that are reared in isolation are yellow-green, and become reddish brown in the final stages. If, however, ten to twenty individuals are put together in a cage they become velvety black as they do in *Laphygma*. Also as in *Laphygma*, the dark caterpillars are more active than the solitary ones, consume more food, develop more quickly, and more homogeneously. All sorts of differences are enumerated by Hirata (1953).

Iwao and his colleagues have carried matters further, and shown that crowding together also affects diapause. In contrast to what happens in most insects, artificially shortening the daylight does not bring on diapause in solitary caterpillars, whereas they enter into diapause if even one other is put into the same rearing tube. A group of caterpillars immediately becomes to some degree sensitive to the length of daylight, and if this is shortened, then more of them go into diapause. Neither the yellowing of the plant host, nor contamination with excreta have any effect on diapause; vibratory stimuli applied to the solitary caterpillar have no effect.

It seems clear that the group effect is brought about by stimuli – visual, tactile or chemical – originating from the other caterpillars present.

It was Zaher (1961) who made the first observation of how grouping of the larvae could affect the morphological or physiological characteristics of the *adult* insects. Up to the present time this effect has been disputed, or even denied, and it was more or less agreed that the moths derived from gregarious caterpillars did not

Figure 31. Variation of a number of biological characteristics of the caterpillar of *Leucania separata* according to the density under which it is reared.

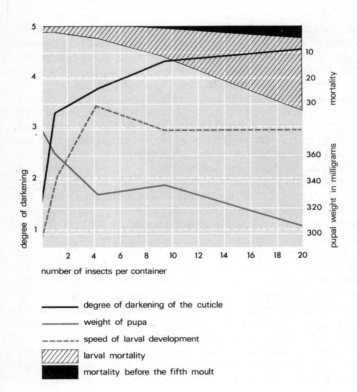

degree of darkening of the cuticle

weight of pupa

speed of larval development

larval mortality

mortality before the fifth moult

differ from those derived from solitary ones. All the same, in *Prodenia litura* the adults arising from gregarious caterpillars showed some modifications of bodily proportions: for example the ratio of coxa-femur is greater, and for another thing the females have more eggs. In these respects they recall the migratory locusts discussed earlier.

Figure 32.
Some biological consequences of
crowding in *Naranga aenescens*.

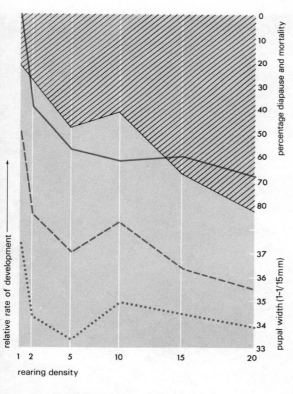

percentage diapause and mortality

relative rate of development

pupal width (1−1/15mm)

rearing density

—————— percentage diapause
− − − − speed of larval development
• • • • • • breadth of mesothorax
mortality during larval period

Adults of the store beetle *Tribolium castaneum*, which has been the subject of many population studies. Some of the most interesting have concerned its interaction with a related species *T. confusum* (see page 127).

A close view of a single
tenebrionid beetle. Because
these beetles are so easily bred
in a jar of flour they have
contributed a great deal to
modern population studies.

Group effects in Coleoptera

Only *Tribolium* and *Tenebrio* have been studied. Utida (1956) working with a bruchid beetle living in beans, *Callosobruchus maculatus*, distinguished a form which was ground-living, and another which flew about: now these differences in behaviour are induced by differences in density of crowding among the larval population. The flying form is reared in more dense aggregation, lays many eggs, and lives longer at low temperatures.

In *Ptinus tectus* there is a special sensitivity to the presence of even a single other individual. The smallest quantity of flour which, with a trace of yeast, will suffice for complete development is three centigrams and this gives rise to miniature adult beetles; the quantity must be increased to thirty centigrams to get the beetles full size. But this holds good only for single individuals, because if several are grouped together development is retarded by about 4% for the same amount of flour per individual. If a group of eight individuals is to produce normal adults it must be provided with up to five grams of food per insect! This is more than ten times the amount that suffices for a solitary larva. The group effect in *Ptinus* is interesting because it very quickly becomes a mass effect, even at relatively low densities (Green and Knight, 1945).

Group effects in social or subsocial insects

Social insects as such are not part of our subject, but we cannot avoid saying something about them in relation to group effects. Hive-bees, ants and termites cannot live in isolation, but die in a few hours, or at most a few days. This is the strongest group effect known, but its mechanism is hardly understood. In the hive-bee it seems that isolation sets up a considerable disturbance; on this first point we are almost sure. Could it be then that the insect exhausts its reserves far too quickly, and cannot replenish them, even though supplied with food and water? On this hypothesis, communal life acts as a tranquiliser!

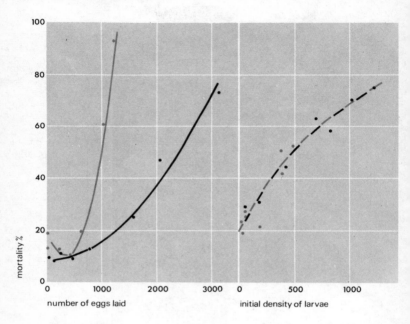

Figure 33. The initial density of either eggs or larvae has a noticeable effect on the percentage mortality during this phase of growth in *Callosobruchus chinensis*. Green line, flying form of the beetle; black line the non-flying form (after Utida, 1956).

Some time ago I studied the very small ant *Leptothorax*, which is very active when it is alone, and its activity can be registered easily by the use of a 'microactograph', with an optical lever. The presence of several other ants, and above all the presence of a queen, reduced this activity enormously. Here, therefore, the idea that the presence of others may have a tranquilising effect may perhaps have some serious basis. In that case the social insects must be at the opposite pole to the grasshoppers, whose metabolism is speeded up by crowding together.

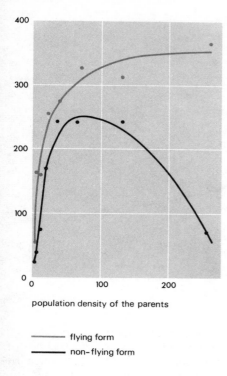

Figure 34. More effects of crowding in *Callosobruchus chinensis*: relationship between the population density of the parents and the number of the offspring (after Utida, 1906).

population density of the parents

— flying form
— non-flying form

Different species grouped together

It follows clearly from all this that to the relationships of predator/prey and of concurrence, which we have already looked at, we must add relationships of one insect to another by juxtaposition, or the effects of proximity. We shall see in what follows that proximity effects should not be forgotten, not even when it is several species that are being put together. They may have a great effect on each other, while appearing to show the greatest indifference.

Figure 35. Group-effects in *Callosobruchus quadrimaculatus*: how the number of eggs laid per female is related to the population density. Green line, flying form of the species; black line the non-flying form (after Utida, 1956).

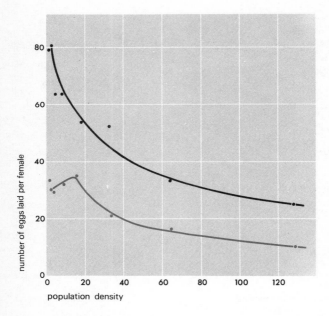

In a piece of work that is already getting old, Crombie (1944–7) reared *Rhizopertha* in media conditioned by *Oryzaephilus* or by *Sitotroga*. *Oryzaephilus* was reared in media conditioned by *Tribolium* and *vice versa*. Now the medium conditioned by *Rhizopertha* noticeably raised the fecundity of *Oryzaephilus*, the very opposite of the struggle for existence, as it is envisaged. Park, Gregg and Lutherman (1941), in the course of making mixed rearings, stated that *Tribolium* does not hinder the development of *Gnathoceros*, but the reverse is not true. *Trogoderma* is almost completely inhibited by *Tribolium*. *Gnathoceros* inhibits *Trogoderma*, if it is more numerous at the beginning, but the reverse happens if it is less numerous than the *Trogoderma*.

The workers of Park's school quickly realised that they were

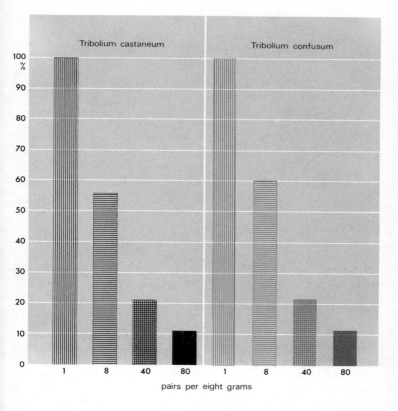

Figure 36. Crowding together reduces the total number of eggs laid
by females of *Tribolium*. In each of the two examples, the total
number of eggs laid by two females confined in 8 gm of food-material
is taken as 100 % (after Birch, Park and Frank).

tackling a problem that was a little too difficult, and they limited
themselves to the effect of putting together two species of the same
genus: *Tribolium confusum* and *T. castaneum*. For a start the two
species were compared in the rate of development of their respective populations. *T. castaneum* showed a fecundity greater than
that of *confusum* at all densities, but this fecundity is reduced in the

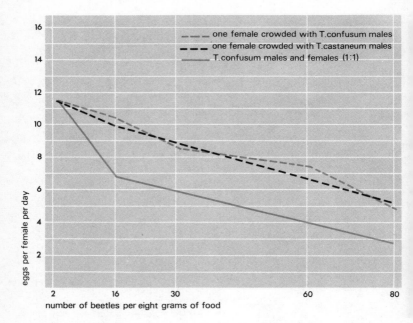

Figure 37. The egg-production of a single female of *Tribolium confusum* is reduced by crowding, even if the other insects present are not other females of its own kind (after Birch, Park and Frank).

same proportions in both species when the density of crowding is increased. When the female of one species is grouped with a number of males her fecundity diminishes much less than in the presence of a mixture of males and females. In the first case cannibalism seems to be the only reason for the drop in fecundity; but in the second case there is another unknown factor, much more significant – possibly the reduction of fertility discovered by Le Gay Brereton (see above). In mixed populations *castaneum* inhibits *confusum*, but not more than *confusum* inhibits itself; but *confusum* inhibits *castaneum* more than *castaneum* inhibits itself. So it seems that *confusum* must inhibit directly the *fecundity* of *castaneum* (Birch, Park, Frank, 1951).

Larvae of the weevil *Calandra granaria* inside a grain of wheat. *Calandra*, like *Tenebrio*, has been widely bred for use in experimental studies of insect populations.

In prolonged competition *castaneum* ends up by eliminating *confusum* but this requires a very protracted period, perhaps several years. It is true that the one species or the other can be favoured by different combinations of temperature and pressure, to which the two species react differently. All the same in a combination under which one of the two species ought to win hands down (for example *castaneum*) it is regularly noticed that a small percentage of the colonies give rise to the opposite results, where *confusum* gets the better of *castaneum*.

Park and Lloyd (1953) asked themselves whether natural selection might not have produced a strain of *confusum* that could win the struggle; but this hypothesis is improbable, because

The weevil, *Calandra oryzae*,
attacking grains of rice. This
insect is used in the laboratory
in experimental population studies.

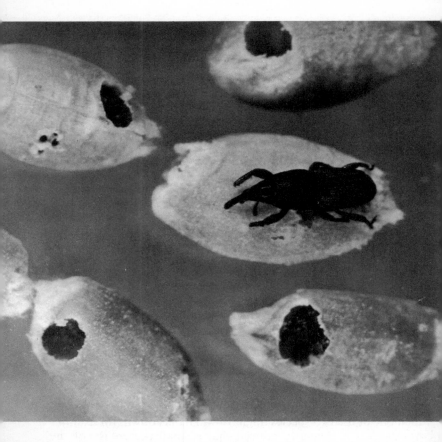

Tribolium reproduces slowly and would have had only a very
small number of generations from which such a selection could
have been made. So then these authors isolated successful strains of
confusum in order to put them again into the presence of *castaneum*
from the stock culture. They did not get any new results in this way,

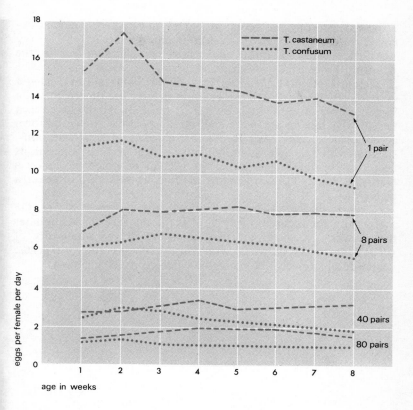

Figure 38. Graphs of egg-production per day over a period of eight weeks, when different numbers of beetles are confined in 8 gm of food material. Crowding drastically reduces egg-production throughout the period.

either in the proportion of strains of dominant *confusum*, which remained the same, or in the time that the *castaneum* took to overcome the *confusum*. Everything depended on the original conditions, which are still undetermined. Moreover within this discovery of 'winning strains in a losing stock' there are a number of most interesting prospects: may there not be here a new mechanism through which natural selection can operate?

Another cause of quite unexpected complication lies in the recently discovered existence of *biological races* in *Tenebrio* (Leclercq, 1950), in *Calandra oryzae* (Birch, 1944) and in *Calandra granaria* (Richards, 1948). For example in *Tenebrio* the weights of a large number of individuals do not lie on a Gaussian curve, even though the insects are reared as far as possible under uniform conditions. Leclercq therefore made a series of trial selections, starting with the lightest individuals, and after four generations succeeded in obtaining a strain the weights of which did lie on a Gaussian curve. Using the same method he was able to select a heavy race.

Calandra oryzae also exists in two races, differing in size. On maize, at a temperature of 29°C, it is the big race that eliminates the smaller; on wheat the reverse occurs. If the small race of *Calandra* is placed on wheat with *Rhizopertha* it is the *Rhizopertha* which dominates at 32°C and the *Calandra* at 29°C (Birch).

4 Populations in nature

I have stressed in the foregoing chapters how much interest a cultivated field can have as a subject for ecological observations and experiments, and I regretted that relatively few research workers have bothered about it up to the present. But an exception must be made of the Germans, whose bioclimatic and entomological studies on the cultivated field are by way of becoming famous.

Long before the Second World War Tamm and his collaborators had thus installed at their celebrated research station at Berlin-Dahlem a veritable 'bioclimatological observatory'. Surrounding a central building had been sown all the crop plants that are cultivated in Germany in the open field. Innumerable thermo-electric elements measured temperature at all points, and were linked to the observatory by a network of cables. There recorders worked for years and years, reeling off miles of graphs. Thanks to the German school, the microclimate of fields of clover, of wheat, of potatoes, of barley, of buck-wheat . . . all are completely recorded.

Later, shortly after the Second World War we have seen blossoming another series of such entomological studies, which we owe most particularly to the team of workers grouped round Tischler of Kiel. This school has published on fields of clover, alfalfa, potato, and sugar-beet monumental monographs, which unfortunately are rather inaccessible; and in particular the work of Frage on the phytosociology of a field of clover and alfalfa, and the enormous dissertation of Heydemann on the fields of barley and of potatoes have never been published, at least to my knowledge.

Truth to tell, and without wishing to repeat what has been said in an earlier chapter, I do not think that the sampling methods used by these authors were very rigorous, and several people, such as Boness, have not hesitated to admit this. But the vast accumulation of observations over several years, and for a large number of biotopes, results in our knowing the fauna of certain fields, and especially that of a field of alfalfa, incomparably better than we know the fauna of many other biotopes.

In this connection, some readers may wonder why so many

authors show so much interest in fields of alfalfa, when at first sight these seem no more important than, say, a field of wheat. The reasons are purely practical ones. The field of alfalfa is a perennial crop, and in practice remains at the disposal of the research worker from the beginning of spring until the end of autumn; whereas the 'life' of wheat is very much less. That is why we now know the field of alfalfa so well that the initial survey work can be considered done. Many details remain, and will remain, to be cleared up; but the last few years have brought more progress than the twenty that preceded them.

A brief glance at the German methods

At the risk of repeating myself I am going to mention here certain characteristics of the methods of the German authors, which will help us to understand their conclusions better, and eventually to assess them. Schnell, Boness and a number of others have often used the sweep net, which we have seen to have numerous and serious defects. Moreover Balogh and Loksa themselves commented that three of the beetles that are commonest in alfalfa – *Apion oestimatum*, *Sitona puncticollis* and *Sitona humeralis* – are not caught in the net, very likely because they let themselves fall down before the net can enclose them, or else they are not even at the tips of the plants at the time of collecting.

On the other hand, Boness on alfalfa, and Prilop on beetroot have made an extensive use of Moericke traps, green or yellow, placed at different heights. As we have seen, this type of trap, which leads to the capture of an impressive quantity of insects, has not been studied in a way commensurate with its results; and though it catches a lot of insects, we do not know exactly why or how.

In contrast, for the fauna of the *epigaion*, that is to say that fauna which moves about over the ground between the stems. Boness and Heydemann have made extensive use of Barbar traps, and Heydemann has gone quite a long way with his experimental studies. Remember that these are wide-mouthed bottles, filled with

135

Table 10 Catches in a Barber trap with transparent and opaque cover (after Heyclemann).

| | Number of insects caught | |
	Glass cover	Lead cover
Lasius niger	7	1
Silpha obscura	10	5
Carabus auratus	37	42
Agonum mulleri	8	0
A. dorsale	13	19
Bembidion lampros	8	1
Ophonus pubescens	9	0
Pterostichus vulgaris	15	5
Micryphantidae	84	15
Astilbus	17	17
Staphylinidae	22	7
Total	296	186
Total Coleoptera	160	108

formalin and water, and sunk level with the soil. Either 4% formalin or ethylene glycol may be used. A certain number of factors have a great effect on the number of insects caught: for example whether the trap is sheltered from the rain, with a sheet of metal, as is usually done. Actually the roof ought to be transparent, and table 10 shows what a difference this makes.

Degree of significance of sampling methods

As I have already had occasion to remark, rare are the entomologists who seriously ask themselves whether their sampling methods are significant: that is to say, who ever ask themselves up to what point are their samples representative of the actual population. Now it is this problem that has been a major preoccupation of the two Hungarian entomologists, Balogh and Loksa. What does it matter that the method of catching on sight used by these authors is the most rudimentary that one could imagine? As they themselves have fully taken into account, to throw a metal box, without top or bottom, at random on to the alfalfa, and then to squat beside it, picking up with forceps the insects that one sees, is bound to miss all those that are too small or too quick, and possibly some of the others as well. Moreover Balogh and Loksa limited themselves in practice to the study of Coleoptera and Hemiptera. Nevertheless the discussion that they give of the number of samples, and the minimum surface to be explored is so interesting that it deserves to be kept. Besides, it comes close to many techniques used in the study of plant communities, which have obviously impressed Balogh and Loksa.

Study of plant communities – phytosociology

Among ordinary people, and even among some scientists, the good old systematic botany arouses scarcely any interest, or at most an amused indulgence. Drawings and caricatures have popularised an image of a gentle lunatic, who wanders through the woods and meadows, with his green tin vasculum slung round his shoulder, full of plants destined to end their existence in his herbarium. Scientists have had quite sound reasons for their opinion: botanical classification is practically finished, a dead science, at least for the higher plants. As near as makes no matter we know *all* the plants in the world, whereas we are a long way from knowing all the insects, for example. And in the immense

General Herbarium of the *Muséum de Paris*, it is not uncommon to find, for example, a Chinese student, deep in the study of the plants of his native land.

But from another point of view, can one ever say that any branch of science is closed? If we have catalogued all the plants in the world, and *a fortiori* all those of France, what can we do with the list? It was in this way that there arose the famous Zurich–Montpellier school of phytosociology, of which the 'chef d'orchestre' is Braun-Blanquet. Elementary observation shows that the same plants do not grow everywhere. Plant associations are quite different in the Normandy pastures, under the sea-winds of Brittany, or in the high Cevennes, and a study of such associations is the essence of the work of the new phytosociologists.

It is not easy either to delimit or to define these associations. They must be counted exactly – easy when dealing with plants, which do not try to escape like insects – and then to apply statistics. In practice one puts down a rectangle of string on the plot to be prospected, and counts all the plants inside it. It then becomes possible by comparison of different areas to come to the most interesting conclusions about the nature of the terrain, and the degree of evolution of its flora. For instance, if a cultivated field is allowed to tumble down to waste, the distinctive flora of the forest (if it is near to a forest) does not become established instantly. Before the stable state (what the phytosociologists call the 'climax vegetation') is reached, a series of transitional stages follow one another over a number of years, and it is these that the Zurich–Montpellier School has taught us how to discover. The applications of phytosociology are very many, but they do not concern us here. Let us return to Balogh and Loksa.

Dominance; mean; Renkonen Number, etc. . . .

The two Hungarian authors tried to determine the *abundance* (the mean density of a species); the *dominance* (percentage of a particular species among the total captures); the *degree of constancy* (percentage in all the samples – each sample for a given day being considered as a unit); the *dispersion* across the field; and naturally the *seasonal variation*.

For example their metal box at first measured 25 × 25 cm and they found there on the average five or six species of beetles. This mean number of species remains the same whether one studies ten or fifty squares. With a box of 50 × 50 cm, the surface being four times as great, on the average ten species are to be found, that is only twice as many as before. Inside a one-metre square, sixteen times as great, we have thirty-five species, a factor of seven. If a square-size of one quarter of a metre is assumed, and the number of squares is plotted against the percentage of the total number of species it appears that one would need to study fifty such squares 25 × 25 cm to obtain 100% of the species on alfalfa. But with *only ten squares* one comes very close to 100% for the beetles the most abundant and most frequent on alfalfa in Hungary (*Apion oestimatum, Halyzia 14-punctata, H. 18-guttata, Cryptophagus punctipennis, Tachyporus nitidulus, Enicmus transversus*).

Balogh and Loksa tried to calculate also the *degree of identity* and of *homogeneity* of the captures by the method of Jaccard (Jaccard Number). Unfortunately the calculations are a little too long to be reproduced here. Briefly, one should consider twelve areas of 50 × 50 cm and compare each of them with all the others, without omitting any possible combination: this gives a certain number of combination-pairs, which are written in separate compartments. Then the number of species common to two neighbouring compartments is divided by the total number of species, and the whole multiplied by one hundred. Then, comparing the quotients in all the compartments, one obtains the figure 2·75 for the vegetation layer, and 2·56 for the epigaion. The number of species common to all the compartments is therefore between two and three; it may be expressed differently by saying that the Jaccard Number, or numbers of identical compartments, is 28% for the vegetation layer and 18% for the epigaion. These figures are low, no doubt as a result of the presence of many stray species.

Balogh and Loksa, their interest particularly aroused by the small number of species naturally present on alfalfa, then decided that the Jaccard Number is not very useful, and gives an untrustworthy picture of the relative importance of species. They introduced another consideration, that of the Renkonen Number, which refers not only to the qualitative status of the fauna (i.e. the number of species) but also to the number of individuals (i.e. the dominance). When considering only a square of 50 × 50 cm in the vegetational layer, the dominance found in the square is practically the same as the dominance in the whole field. But it is not the same as for the epigaion. The two authors then compared dominance and degree of homogeneity of the epigaion and of the vegetational layer. We shall see a little later the results of this comparison; but let us begin by taking as example the field of alfalfa, and see how we proceed at the present day to make a complete study of a cultivated field.

The plants of the field of alfalfa

While the plant-carpet is obviously more homogeneous in a cultivated field than elsewhere, it is not completely so, and all the plants that make their appearance in a field of alfalfa attract their own set of insects. It is desirable therefore to do a little phytosociology in connection with alfalfa, and Frage applied himself to this task (1951) in a monograph that unfortunately, as I have just said, has not been published. The flora to be listed is that of fields in Schleswig Holstein and North Germany. From the first year on there appeared in the alfalfa plants characteristic of grassland associations, and these associations tend to develop particularly where the alfalfa is thin. They are particularly distinct in old plots of alfalfa. Frage distinguished the species, listed in table 11 (page 140), in order of frequency.

Every month between March and November at least some of these species are in flower. But in fields where alfalfa is especially vigorous most of the plants are almost stifled in summer.

Table 11 Plants occurring in old plots of alfalfa, in order of frequency (after Frage).

Poa annua	*Rumex crispus*
Capsella bursa pastoris	*Galium aparine*
Cirsium arvense	*Stellaria media*
Taraxacum officinale	*Cerastium cespitosum*
Polygonum aviculare	*Tussilago farfara*
Plantago lanceolata	*Chenopodium album*
Sonchus oleraceus	*Achillaea millefolia*
Myosotis arenaria	*Matricaria chamomilla*
Viola tricolor	*Matricaria inodora*
Ranunculus acer	*Sinapis arvensis*
Equisetum arvense	*Lamium purpureum*
Plantago major	

The microclimate of the alfalfa

Alfalfa comes into the category of the microclimates of low plants, which we have dealt with in the first chapter. The alfalfa is characterised by having a zone of transition, corresponding to the entire thickness of the vegetational layer, in which all abrupt variations are smoothed out. It will be noted that the relative humidity in a field of clover or of alfalfa with leaves and stems interlocked (or 'gekreuzte', as the Germans say) rises even in

Figure 39. A light-trap operated at Rothamsted Experimental Station, England, during the years 1933–6 collected an average of 3902 individuals per year, belonging to 176 species. The graph shows the number of species in the catch which have, say, five individuals, the number with ten individuals, and so on. The resulting points fall close to the calculated curve of a logarithmic series (green line) (after Williams).

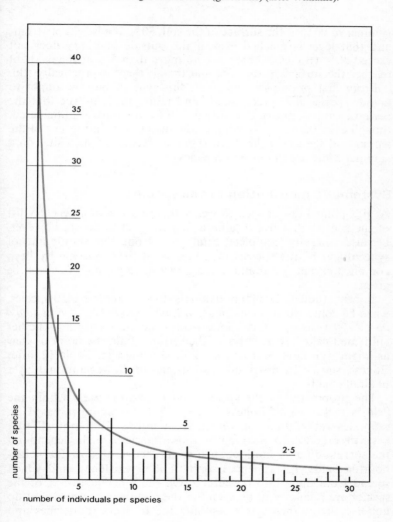

summer to 90 % at the surface of the soil, 80 % at a height of 10 cm; and that level is reached even if the outside humidity does not exceed 30 % (Boness). Moreover no more than 5 % of the daylight reaches the surface of the soil, and the air there is practically still.

From first principles, therefore, this type of biotope ought to favour species that prefer shade and moisture. It is true that the periodic catastrophe of the cutting of the crop must be anticipated, though even then a proportion of the insects can find refuge in the stooks and the ricks; the thermal characteristics of such sites on a summer's day are discussed on pages 164–5.

Systematic distribution of the species

At this point I am obliged to weary the reader with a very dry list of the species that live in alfalfa. It is helpful to do so, however, because a really complete catalogue (from the standpoint of synecology) of the species in a cultivated field, has hardly been compiled except for alfalfa. Such a rare example might as well be given!

Boness studied 120,000 individuals divided among 1450 species, when he compiled this catalogue. *Within a single field can be found up to 790 species*, a fact which makes the author doubt whether cultivated fields are as impoverished from a faunistic point of view as might well have been written a little while ago. Table 12, after Boness, shows the distribution of species in the vegetational layer of alfalfa fields.

The proportion of the species that develop entirely within the field is reckoned by Boness at 75 %, but this figure is based on estimates rather than on direct observations. It is not all that easy in practice to distinguish those species which depend on the surrounding vegetation, such as the hedgerows, or the neighbouring fields, for at least a part of their existence, and which spread from these into the alfalfa. On the other hand 5 % of the species are regularly to be found in the middle of the field, but do not live there: these are essentially the foragers (butterflies and

Table 12 Distribution of species in alfalfa fields

Oligochaeta	7	Thysanoptera	31
Gastropoda	9	Rhynchota	110
Isopoda	5	Hymenoptera	480
Diplopoda	15	Coleoptera	507
Chilopoda	6	Lepidoptera	37
Arachnida	60	Diptera	270
Acari	30	Various other insects	20
Collembola	10	Vertebrates	34

moths, bees, wasps). Finally 20–25% were 'Irrgäste', unintentional visitors, found in the alfalfa only by chance. No doubt the bees could be regarded as unintentional visitors, too:—

Bees and alfalfa – a digression

If you try to introduce into a flower of alfalfa any sharp, pointed object, such as the lead of a pencil, you will set in motion the curious phenomenon known as 'tripping'. As if on a spring, the column which bears the pistils and stamens shoots suddenly out of the centre of the petals, and crashes against the pencil. When a bee tries to forage from the alfalfa the same thing happens to it, and one might almost say it had had a punch on the jaw, if it had a jaw. The bees seem disagreeably surprised at this trick of the flower, and forage from alfalfa without enthusiasm, or not at all: and this is a most serious matter, because the alfalfa is incapable of fertilising itself.

People have therefore tried to make pollination of the alfalfa easier by several devices. The first idea was to swamp the field with bees, and this is easiest to do in North America, where the fields of alfalfa are immense, and are very nearly the only source of food for the bees. In this event, obviously, if one hundred hives are placed in a field that can scarcely sustain fifty, then the honey crop is nil. But that does not matter: special contracts compensate the bee-keepers for the loss of honey. And this formula has succeeded so well that it has given rise to a veritable 'pollination industry', in which the bees are the workpeople. Enormous lorries, loaded with hundreds of hives, plough their way across the USA, awaited with impatience by the farmers and tree-men.

Attempts have been made to rear a race of hive-bees that does not mind the tripping mechanism – since differences in tolerance occur naturally among different strains of bees – or even races of alfalfa in which the sexual column projects in a normal way from the petals. Truth to tell, up to now only a partial success has been achieved in either of these two attempts. So much so that a new technique has begun to be tried, involving the rearing of other Hymenoptera (bumble-bees, among others) which are not put off by the tripping of the flower.

Abundance and Dominance

A fauna is not sufficiently characterised by labelling each species as 'abundant' or 'scarce'. It is necessary to indicate the degree of abundance of each, and this is not always easy. For example according to Schnell, who unfortunately was equipped only with a sweep net, *Sitona lineata* formed 47% of the beetle-fauna; *S. humeralis* 12·9%; *Phytonomus variabilis* 32·5%. Variations were found between different varieties of alfalfa: for instance in Thuringia and in Hungary a variety is cultivated that has tougher leaves, and this seems to affect the abundance of *Phytonomus variabilis*. In the same way *Medicago falcata* was less attacked by *Phytonomus* beetles than either *M. sativa* or *M. media*.

As we have seen, the most thorough study of dominance and abundance has been made by Balogh and Loksa. It is a pity that the fauna of a field of alfalfa in central Europe is very different from the fauna of a field of alfalfa in western Europe, and so only limited comparisons can be drawn. The two Hungarian authors, who were strongly influenced by phytosociology, attempted to define the 'alfalfa biotope' according to which species were dominant there. They found that out of 313 beetles taken from the vegetational layer, 258 were *Apion oestimatum*, and out of 104 predators, the majority were *Halyzia*. The saprophagous beetles living on the ground were essentially made up of *Cryptophagus punctipennis*, *Calathus ambiguus*, and *Microlestes maurus*.

It follows from this that the really important constituents of the biological community (biocenosis) come down to just a few species. On the other hand there are very appreciable differences in *homogeneity* according to whether we look at the vegetational layer or the epigaion. For example if in the vegetational layer we need to examine fifty squares each 25 × 25 cm in order to obtain 100% of the species of beetles present; down on the ground forty such squares will be enough. The population living on the surface of the soil is thus more homogeneous; but the apparent difference may vary according to the method of evaluation that is used, and especially according to whether we take the Renkonen Number or the Jaccard Number.

Characteristics of the alfalfa biocenosis in western Europe (after Boness)

The biocenosis of a field of alfalfa, as far as we know it, calls for certain comments. We have ascertained that 32% of the species are plant-feeders, 20% saprophagous, and 49% carnivorous. We shall see later on that the majority of the plant-feeders are to be found in the vegetational layer, and the majority of the saprophagous forms down on the ground, as is to be expected, since the vegetable debris on which the latter feed falls to the ground. But out of the 510 plant-feeding species, 42, that is to say 8% live exclusively on the leguminous plants (i.e. on the alfalfa), 92 (18%) on various grasses: 268 (52%) are species of open grassland or live on the vegetation surrounding the field of alfalfa; 108 (22%) are polyphagous, but with a preference for cultivated leguminous crops.

It may be said straightaway that *although the species that are adapted to the alfalfa are few in number they are rich in individuals*, while the opposite is true of the species that are present in the field but not adapted specially to leguminous crops. Boness also shows that the greater number of plant-sucking species live in the vegetational layer, and especially in the floral zone. The leaf and stem miners also, of course, live in the vegetational zone. The browsers are to be found for preference on the ground, but with a large number, all the same, in the vegetation.

A good enough idea of the real importance of the quantity of animal matter that lives on the alfalfa crop can be obtained by arranging the species according to their body-length in millimetres, and then multiplying the cube of the length by the number of individuals. This gives a rough idea of their total weight. This quantity is called the 'biomass'; and although it seems comic to compare one kilogram of Carabid beetles with one kilo of flies, this is a concept that has proved to be both interesting and useful in ecology (table 13).

The biggest plant-feeding insects, with so many parasites living at their expense, together form the most considerable mass of living matter in the vegetational layer. Near the ground, on the other hand, the small forms predominate, with the saprophagous and parasitic forms. Another oddity from the quantitative standpoint is that according to Scherney, a Carabid beetle in captivity eats every day from 1·3 to 3·4 times its own weight. A beetle weighing 500 mg therefore eats sixty grams in its four months of active life. Now there is almost one Carabid for every 30 square metres: therefore the Carabids in one hectare must eat 20 kilograms of living matter every day, and this ignores other predators.

Table 13 Abundance and biomass of insects living on alfalfa

	Length-groups (in mm)					
	1	1–2	2–4	4–8	8–16	16–32
Plant-feeders						
Abundance (thousands)	16·0	46·0	24·0	12·0	1·5	0·5
Biomass	0·05	1·2	5·0	17·8	18·0	58·0
Saprophagous						
Abundance	20·1	50·7	27·6	1·3	0·3	0·01
Biomass	0·7	8·6	43·0	17·0	29·8	0·9
Predators						
Abundance	1·3	44·7	39·3	12·3	2·1	0·3
Biomass	0·003	1·2	8·1	20·1	19·1	41·5
Parasites						
Abundance	43·3	49·3	6·7	0·6		
Biomass	4·0	34·0	38·0	24·0		

The faunal layers

Boness, like the majority of the German ecologists, distinguishes between: the fauna of the soil (euedaphon); the surface of the ground (epigaion); and the vegetational layer (epiedaphon) – within which at certain times he differentiates the floral zone. We

148

shall hardly be concerned with the euedaphon, the fauna of which, in the alfalfa field, does not seem to be any different from that in grassland generally, and which has been studied by a number of authors, including Kruger (1952) and von Baudissin (1952).

Within the epiedaphon, the species are distributed in a very different way in different localities. But Boness himself remarks that he has used different methods of catching his insects, and that these are not comparable with each other. On the surface of the ground are found especially earthworms, Collembola, mites, spiders, Carabid and Staphylinid beetles, ants, hunting wasps, ichneumons, Sciarid and Borborid and Phorid flies, all species which fall quite readily into the Barber traps.

The vegetational layer abounds in Hemiptera, Diptera, weevils, and their parasites; and into the lower layers climb Staphylinids and saprophagous flies from the ground. I have often found Phorids and Sciarids just at the limit of the floral zone.

With the help of sticky traps, Boness found out that although the majority of insects in flight are at about 60–70 cm up in the air, Thysanoptera and Staphylinids in contrast fly close to the ground. Parasitic Hymenoptera, Cecidomyidae, Sciaridae, Phoridae and Lonchopteridae more often fly among the stems than in the floral zone. I have used sticky traps with the object of finding out about the faunal layers, and I have not found the same distribution as Boness found. Phorids and Lonchopterids appeared much more numerous in the floral zone. Braconids, Chalcids and Sciarids were to be found in the same numbers in the floral zone and between the stems. During the day the Cecidomyids in flight were more numerous in the lowest layer.

As for weevils in the alfalfa, according to Schnell they are especially abundant in the lowest layer, and even on the surface of the ground, since they are often found in the Barber traps. Phytonomids also turn up frequently in the vegetational layer; and *Otiorrhynchus* weevils are not found in the Barber traps. Balogh and Loksa state that in the month of June *Sitona* is most abundant in the lowest level of the epiedaphon. Nevertheless the sampler has

always given us a significant number of weevils in the floral zone. If the German authors, and most especially Schnell, have hardly found any there, may this not be because they use sweep nets for catching them? Most weevils readily fall to the ground at the slightest vibration of the stem, and so it is not surprising that they are most easily caught in Barber traps.

Edges v. middle

The German authors (Boness, Heydemann, Schnell, Prilop) stress very much the differences between the middle of the field and the edges, and I have been equally astonished at these differences. Sun-loving, heat-loving and drought-loving species generally prefer the middle of the field, but sometimes the edges are richer in both individuals and species.

Table 14 gives a comparison of the fauna of the marginal five metres with that of thirty metres inside (after Boness, modified). Almost all species are more numerous round the edges of the field, except for the Aphids, Collembola, thrips and leaf-hoppers. There are hardly any short-horned grasshoppers except near the edges. Moreover many species hibernate outside the field altogether, in the hedgerows, and their re-entry in spring can easily be followed by using Barber traps.

According to Schnell, weevils of the genus *Apion* always decrease in numbers from the edge of the field towards the middle. The same is true of *Sitona* and Phytonomids, but with some exceptions. I also found many more thrips, Chalcid and Proctotrupid wasps and Phorid flies near the edges, and many fewer Sciarid flies.

Conditions at night

Here I cannot entirely agree with Boness, at least as far as the nocturnal distribution of the fauna is concerned. Although the maximum number of species in flight occurs, just as he says, round the middle of the day, in contrast we have several times recorded a

Table 14 Comparison of the fauna of the marginal five metres of a field with that of thirty metres inside (figures expressed as a percentage of the fauna in the middle of the field).

	Surface of ground %	Plant layer %
Gasteropod molluscs	—	220
Isopods (woodlice)	380	—
Spiders	133	165
Mites	130	165
Collembola	70	109
Thrips	—	70
Heteroptera	—	480
Leaf-hoppers	—	76
Aphids	—	93
Adult beetles	142	135
Beetle larvae	130	280
Adult flies	120	100
Adult Hymenoptera	170	190

nocturnal drop in numbers, shown equally by suction traps and the selecter, and we do not know how to explain it. Using the sweep net, on the contrary, Boness found *more* insects. It is not easy to find an explanation for such a radical divergence. One suggestion was that the insects in the plants might fall to the ground at night, but this could not be confirmed because we were not using Barber traps at the same time as we were collecting in the plants.

According to Boness spiders and thrips are present in larger numbers in the middle of the day, and diminish greatly in the evening, no doubt because they move down the stems to take shelter. Hemiptera are most numerous in the morning. Collembola, Staphylinidae (and especially their larvae), snails, and minute beetles (*Atomaria;* Lathrididae) climb up at night, and spend the night at the top of the stems; often they disappear completely from the tops during the day.

Leaf-hoppers and aphids do not show such well-defined nocturnal movements. Among weevils *Phytonomus punctatus* and *Otiorhynchus* are essentially nocturnal. *Sitona lineatus* and *griseus* are more active by day in the spring. In summer, when the sun is hotter, they are to be seen mostly in the mornings and evenings, according to the observations of a number of authors; but according to Schnell beetles can perfectly well be found in the middle of the hottest days moving about in great numbers over the alfalfa. All the same they can also be found hiding between the clods of earth, so clearly the behaviour of these beetles is governed by a number of local factors.

Flight

It happens that expert fliers such as the muscoid flies are caught in great numbers in the evening and at night. Dolichopodid flies, and the Psocid fly *Lachesilla* particularly in the morning, and in the early afternoon. Also in the early afternoon, but continuing later in the day, are thrips and frit flies; and in the evening most of the beetles, and the Borborid and Cecidomyid flies. Aphids seem to have two peaks in their curve of flight activity, morning and afternoon; the Heteroptera, Homoptera and Psyllids fly in the second half of the day.

Like Boness, we also have caught Cecidomyids, Hemiptera, Heteroptera and frit flies most particularly at the end of the afternoon, about five o'clock. On the other hand we did not get the same results as he did for *Drosophila*, leaf-hoppers, many Cecidomyids and *Sitona*, all of which we found most active at night, about an hour before midnight.

Seasonal variations

As Boness says, it is odd to note the disparity between the growth of population on the ground and among the plants. The peak population of insects among the plants coincides more or less with the peak of plant growth (in July), whereas on the ground the peak population of insects occurs in April–May, a little in advance of the plant peak.

One might, like Boness, study the effects of the seasons separately. *The Winter season* (from December to February and sometimes into March) clearly supports only a reduced fauna. However as long as the cold is not too great a certain number of animals remain active: Gamasiform mites, spiders, larvae of Carabid beetles (*Nebria brevicollis*) and adult beetles (*Simplocaria semistriata*) some Staphylinids, some Collembola and some Sciarids.

The Spring season (April–May, beginning sometimes at the end of March) is characterised by the full development of the vegetation, which is attained in May. The Collembola and most of the spiders also reach their peak then. The Gamasiform mites drop back and are replaced by the Trombidiiform mites, especially on sandy soils. The beetles come out of hibernation, and their number swells enormously, especially *Carabus*, *Phytonomus*, *Sitona*, *Agonum dorsale*, *Trechus 4-striatus*, *Silpha tristis*. In among the plants those species predominate that hibernate as adults: weevils, Halticinae, *Meligethes*, thrips, *Sminthurus viridis*. Among Diptera, the Nematocera are specially numerous: Bibionidae, Sciaridae, Chironomidae, and the first generation of Cecidomyidae, such as *Contarinia medicaginis* and *Dasyneura ignorata*. A few species are also to be found which have hibernated in the soil as larvae or pupae (Chloropid and Agromyzid flies).

Early Summer, in June, is marked by the first flowers of the alfalfa, and also, as the month wears on, by the first hay crop. Among Carabid beetles *Nebria brevicollis* (on heavy soil) and *Pterostichus vulgaris* begin to predominate. Saprophagous beetles (Lathrididae, *Atomaria*, Hydrophilidae) appear among the vegetable debris. This is the time when the larvae of *Phytonomus* climb up on to the alfalfa, sometimes in incredible numbers, as was shown by Chauvin and Lecomte, using the sampler, *Macrosiphum pisi* swarms everywhere, and *Bryobia pretiosa*, *Tylus corrigiolatus*, many Dolichopodid and Empid flies, all appear. On the other hand the adults of those plant-feeding beetles that hibernate will disappear.

High Summer, in July–August, when the alfalfa is in full flower, almost strangling the weeds, provides a second mowing between the end of July and the beginning of August, and a third at the end of August or the beginning of September. On the ground Collembola and mites fall to a minimum; ants and parasitic Hymenoptera increase greatly; 'microcoleoptera' remain numerous. In among the plants the number of individual insects grows, especially the numbers of Heteroptera, leaf-hoppers and thrips. It is in August that the parasitic Hymenoptera, which Lecomte and I caught in such great numbers in suction traps, reach their peak. The Cecidomyidae and other mining Diptera have their second and then their third generation, and aphids, under favourable conditions, increase enormously.

Late Summer, in September, often coincides with a vigorous growth of alfalfa following its last mowing. On the ground, spiders, Gamasiform mites and Collembola reach a second maximum, but not such a high one as they had in spring. Plant-feeding beetles (*Apion*, *Sitona*) pass into the adult stage. Among flies are found *Scatophaga*, Sciaridae and Chironomidae.

The Autumn season is only fully under way during October. On the ground Diptera and Hymenoptera migrate in search of shelter. The saprophagous forms such as Sepsidae, Phoridae, Borboridae, *Lonchoptera*, *Drosophila*, all develop strongly in the vegetable debris. *Nebria brevicollis* is the dominant Carabid beetle.

Figure 40. A pictorial representation of
the development of *Sitona lineata* through
the year (after Müller, 1956, in Tischler).

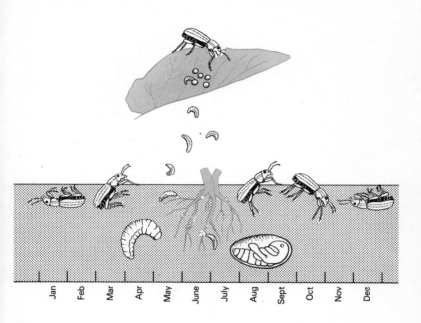

In November the true winter species, such as *Simplocaria* and
the Gamasid mites, begin to increase in numbers.

Our classification of the seasonal changes is a little different
from that of Boness, no doubt because we were without the many
species that could be caught in Barber traps. We found aphids
at all seasons, though it is true they were few after mid-March,
whereas Boness recorded the great populations of *Macrosiphum
pisi* only in the month of June. On the other hand, like Boness, we
found the microcoleoptera very early, and *Sitona* all the year round.
Phytonomus adults were caught only at the end of spring among
the plants, and disappeared in July (at least those belonging to the
first generation; the second generation has its maximum in
September–October). *Apion* is abundant only in spring.

Hibernation

It would be a good thing if the effect of winter on the field of alfalfa could be adequately described, but there still remains the problem of studying all the species that are invisible, because they are hidden away in their winter quarters. According to Boness about 15% of the species found in alfalfa hibernate in the egg stage, 25% as larvae, 20% as pupae, and 35% as adults. Five to ten per cent are to be found near to the underground stems and roots of plants, most of these on the outer edges of the field, such as thrips, Chalcids, Halticinae, etc. In contrast, *Macrosiphum pisi* passes the winter in the middle of the field in the form of a winter egg stuck to a stem. Sixty per cent of the other species hide in the soil, or under vegetable debris on the surface; 30–35% go deeper into the soil: mites; Collembola; larvae and pupae of Diptera, Coleoptera, Lepidoptera, and thrips; and adult beetles such as Staphylinidae.

Fifty per cent of the species migrate more or less far outside the field, but some of the weevils stay in the field, or do not go far away. *Apion* mostly goes into the hedgerows, and hides there under tufts of grass, or in vegetable debris, on top of the hedge, or along its slopes. Which side of the field is selected depends on its orientation in relation to rain and to the prevailing wind: the east or south side is generally preferred (Tischler). The top of the hedge often contains great numbers of weevils, but the foot of the hedge is almost completely left alone.

Finally, *Sitona lineatus* and *Apion virens* may be found in quite large numbers, even in the middle of the field near the roots.

The Heteroptera, and the Chrysomelid and Coccinellid beetles disappear from the field almost completely during the winter, as do most of the Carabidae, Silphidae and many other adult beetles. Many spiders seem equally able to quit the field in winter, but this is not quite certain.

This movement into hibernation, which is mostly limited to the immediate surroundings of the field, usually takes place on foot, as is shown both by observation and by trapping; all the more so

Figure 41. Three ways in which field insects hibernate. Those which go to a completely different locality: 1, *Lygrus*; 2, *Meligethes*; 3, *Aelia*; 4, *Coccinella*; 5, *Haltica*. Those which go only a little way outside the field: 6, *Cassida*; 7, *Phyllotreta*; 8, *Apion*; 9, *Lerme*; 10, *Amara*. Those remaining in the field over winter: 11, *Phytonomus punctatus*; 12, *Agrotis segetum*.

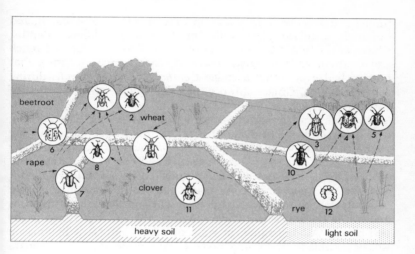

since at this time of year the ability to fly is reduced by the lower temperature. All the same *Meligethes*, *Longitarsus*, *Ceutorrhynchus*, Mirid bugs, thrips, the Diptera, and many of the Hymenoptera, all migrate on the wing, as is shown by sticky traps and Moericke traps.

Unsolved problems

The above account may seem conclusive, and may give the reader the impression that all the problems of locating the insects in winter have been solved. This is not true at all; on the contrary hibernation presents some curious biological problems. These concern not so much fields of alfalfa (at least as far as I know), as fields of colza, for example. At a time when repeated insecticidal treatments were ruining bee-keepers whose bees fed on the colza, I was obliged to study the insects attacking this plant, and especially *Ceuthorrhynchus*. Now they hibernate as adults, and in a single field of colza there may be millions of these beetles, sometimes two or

158

three per flower. Well, in winter, in spite of very careful search, and hundreds of soil samples in different places, and to different depths, I have never found a single one of them. Enquiry among French and German entomologists disclosed, to my great surprise, that no one had ever found a single *Ceuthorrhynchus assimilis* during winter, though some had occasionally found other species of *Ceuthorrhynchus*.

Now this strange example is not unique. My friend Chaboussou, who is Director of a field station, told me that he had been studying over a period of years a species of *Telephorus* which devastated the apple-trees in Bigorre. Over several hundreds of hectares every piece of apple-blossom was being attacked by several *Telephorus*, and like the *Ceuthorrhynchus*, many millions of these insects were concentrated into quite a small area. Their larvae are carnivorous and live in the soil where they hibernate: this much is found in the text-books. All the same, in spite of all his efforts, Chaboussou was never able to find a single one. Furthermore, if these larvae are carnivorous there must at some time be a multiplication of their prey on a scale big enough to support such a vast number of *Telephorus*. The fauna of the soil ought, therefore, to show fluctuations of similar magnitude. The entomologists questioned, as mentioned above, replied that they had not observed any fluctuation that could be linked with an invasion of *Telephorus* beetles.

All of which shows, once again, that ecology is a science that is still in its infancy. . . .

How a new field is populated

How do insects become established in an area where alfalfa is growing for the first time? Boness has not tackled this problem, but Schnell has shown a certain interest in it, since he has compared the population in crops of alfalfa one year and four years old. The population remains small for the first year after the sowing, and grows greatly during the next two years, to decrease again as the alfalfa ages. The life-cycle of alfalfa, extending over several years, is particularly favourable to *Otiorrhynchus ligustici*, which itself develops in two years. But after a few years the field of alfalfa is invaded by a number of weeds and the biotope becomes less favourable to the weevils, which steadily decline in numbers.

That is just about all one can say up to the present about how a new field is colonised by insects; as can be seen, it is very little. We want to attack the insect enemies of cultivated plants, and in the great majority of cases we do not even know how the insects become established. . . .

The influence of meteorological factors

Most of the insect species show their greatest activity only in sunny weather. Cloudy, humid weather is particularly unfavourable for the flight of Lepidoptera, Hymenoptera and thrips. In 1952, however, I noted that suction traps could still make captures of small Hymenoptera and Diptera even in heavy rain, provided that the rain did not last long.

Rain seems scarcely to affect the behaviour of *Phytonomus* or of *Sitona;* at most they shelter under leaves when the rain is heavy, but they move about again when it stops. But according to Schnell, *Apion* (with the exception of *A. virens*) are more seriously affected by bad conditions. According to Dunn and Wright (1955) rain brings about a sharp decline in populations of *Macrosiphum pisi*, though the consequences are not so marked in other aphids. This perhaps comes about because *Macrosiphum* lets itself fall on the slightest disturbance, more readily than the other species, and that it can only climb up the stems again with difficulty.

Boness gives several examples of the different climatic structure of one year and another, and of correlated differences in the development of the insect species. Mild winters, for example, may indirectly affect the insect fauna of the alfalfa field by encouraging the growth of weeds (*Poa annua, Taraxacum officinale, Plantago major*). Certain plant-feeding insects can profit from this if they are sufficiently catholic in their taste: for instance various *Sitona*,

Macrosiphum pisi with its parasites and hyperparasites, *Sminthurus viridis;* saprophagous insects such as the larvae of *Lonchoptera*, *Drosophila*, Sepsidae and *Lucilia;* and finally such predators as Syrphid larvae and Nabidae.

In Schleswig Holstein, for example, the year 1953 was characterised by a mild winter, an early and sunny spring, and a mediocre summer. In 1954, in contrast, the winter was dry and quite severe, the spring cold, late and very dry; early summer hot, the rest of the summer cold and very wet. Now it was not until about 12 May 1954 that the alfalfa had an insect population comparable with what it had by 28 April 1953, with many thrips and *Meligethes* beetles. On 28 April 1954 there was still nothing to be seen except a few saprophagous flies. Winter conditions still prevailed up to the end of April in 1954, whereas in 1953, spring had appeared by the end of March. The larvae of *Phytonomus* did not pupate until the middle of July in 1954, though they had pupated by the beginning of the month in 1953. *Tylus corrigiolatus* was in flight in 1954 two or three weeks later than in 1953. On the other hand, *Oscinella frit* and *Contarinia medicaginis* were to be found at about the same time of year in 1953 and in 1954, no doubt because the fact that they have several generations during the year evens out variations of weather.

Mowing as an ecological catastrophe

Mowing of the alfalfa crop provides a magnificent ecological experiment, though rather a catastrophic one. The consequences are similar to those already studied by Boness in relation to the mowing of grassland. There is an immediate increase in the number of insects on the surface of the ground, probably because these have been forcibly driven out of the plants. Yet the catching methods used by Boness and the German workers do not allow very precise comparisons to be made between the state of the fauna before and after mowing. As a result of gross changes in the conditions among the stems the sweep net, the favourite weapon of these collectors, gives even cruder results than usual. How can one compare a

series of catches with the sweep net when the alfalfa is in full growth with those made when it has been cut to a height of a few centimetres only, and is in process of sprouting again? The elasticity of the stems is clearly not the same, nor is the way in which the net approaches the insect; under these conditions estimates of the fauna cannot be other than very approximate.

Table 15 gives the relative number of individuals remaining after mowing. One part of the *Sitona* and of *Phytonomus* is not affected very much by the mowing, because it is already in the soil in the pupal stage. Resting adults can be found after quite a short time in the fully sprouting alfalfa. Schnell compared the two halves of a field of alfalfa, one of which was mown and the other not. After mowing there was a very sharp rise in number of insects in the half that had not been mown (most particularly of *Sitona lineata*, *hispidula* and *humeralis*). A certain amount of return migration of *Sitona* from the intact half was therefore likely to occur.

According to Mühle Fröhlich (1951), *Otiorrhynchus ligustici* is not harmed by the mowing. It seems on the contrary that many weevils are attracted by the young shoots in full sprouting. All the same Boness showed that *Phytonomus* and the Cecidomyidae can be effectively attacked by advancing the time of mowing, the former in particular being caught by the mowing. It must not be forgotten, however, that the same action favours the reproduction of *Macrosiphum pisi*, a great lover of young shoots.

In contrast to the sweep net, the technique of using the sampler and suction traps, as I have done, makes it possible to study without difficulty the consequences of mowing. These show an almost complete disappearance of thrips, largely because the flowers of the alfalfa are all gone; but aphids increase to formidable proportions. Drosophilidae, small saprophagous beetles, Proctotrupid wasps, Sciarid flies, Cicadas, Collembola, and Lygaeid bugs increase very sharply. Chalcid wasps maintain their numbers, but Phorid flies disappear.

It is necessary, however, to distinguish between the immediate and the long-term results of mowing the alfalfa. Eight to ten days

Table 15 Relative numbers of insects after mowing, taking the number before mowing as unity (after Boness).

	Among the plants	On surface of soil
Spiders	0·3	1·8
Mites	4·3	3·5
Thrips	0·9	3·5
Heteroptera	0·7	3·5
Leaf-hoppers	1·8	3·5
Aphids	0·5	3·5
Coleoptera	1·5	2·6
Diptera	1·3	1·0
Hymenoptera	0·7	2·6
Sminthuridae	1·7	10·0
Other Collembola	1·7	0·8
Centipedes	1·7	1·4
Mean	0·95	1·5

afterwards, *Sitona* is not affected, but small beetles and Lygaeid bugs have diminished moderately, and leaf-hoppers and spiders have disappeared. Yet the explosive increase of the aphids starts immediately after the crop is cut. The Collembola, which live very

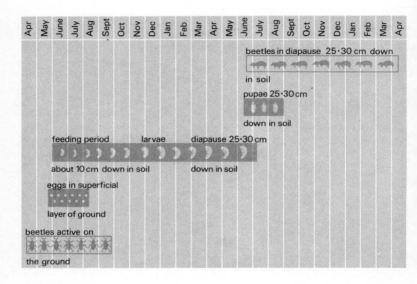

Figure 42. The development of the weevil *Otiorrhynchus ligustici* in the soil, occupies two years (from Tischler, after Palmén and others, 1941).

close to the ground, are not touched. In 1952 it needed four weeks for the small beetles, bugs and Chalcids to recover, and then to exceed their numbers before the mowing took place. The violent outburst of *Sitona* that we also noted is partly brought about by new emergences. Leaf-hoppers and spiders reappear not less than four weeks after the mowing.

Hay-cocks and haystacks

These harbour a very rich and specialised fauna, a great number of animals being attracted by the fermentations that they produce, and which create a special microclimate. Very numerous in such places are mites and saprophagous beetles; and much less numerous are Diptera, Hymenoptera, Hemiptera and above all Collembola.

Many weevils shelter there. Barber traps slipped under hay-cocks catch two or three times as many insects as they do in the open air, and above all the very active damp-loving forms: *Nebria brevicollis*, *Pterostichus vulgaris*, *Tachinus rufipes*, *Atheta*, and other Staphylinidae; later come their larvae, and, alongside them, Gamasid mites, millipedes and centipedes, Phorid and Borborid flies.

About one metre from the ground in the hay-cocks I found enormous numbers of Psocids and of Drosophilidae, as well as a great many *Sitona* which had taken shelter there. Suction traps showed that flying round the hay-cocks were many small beetles, Proctotrupids, Phorids, aphids, and Sciarids; but neither Chironomidae nor Chloropidae, although these could be found in the newly sprouting alfalfa surrounding the hay-cocks.

Are all the fields in one area comparable?

Certainly not; yet in contradiction to what Heydemann found in his potato-field, the nature of the soil does not have much effect on the fauna of alfalfa. It seems that the foliage of the alfalfa, dense and intertwined, levels out the differences more than happens in a field of potato-plants. The insects in the alfalfa are perhaps a little less numerous on heavy soil, but the differences are more marked among those insects on the ground than among those on the plants.

On the other hand, for reasons that are obscure, there may be considerable differences in the numbers of insects between two fields that are only a few kilometres apart. We ourselves found this in the Seine-et-Oise Department. Moreover these differences involved at least half of the important species. The analysis of these differences in relation to the biotope has hardly begun; and moreover the synecology can hardly start seriously until the reasons for these observed differences have been cleared up.

Obviously the differences are still greater if the fields are in distant parts of the country, but we cannot go into lengthy comparisons here. In fact only Balogh and Loksa in Hungary have studied the field of alfalfa with a diligence comparable with that of the German school. In Germany itself there have been some investigations in the south of the country. The grasshoppers are never very numerous, but they always increase towards the south (near Tübingen). Thrips, too, are a little more numerous in the drier regions. In France we have found most of the species that occur in Schleswig. The differences are not enough to be measured.

On the other hand, in Serbia and Macedonia Tanasijevic recorded 37 plant-feeding beetles and 8 Coccinellidae, and of these 45, 32 are found in Germany. Out of 156 species found by Balogh and Loksa, 46 are also found in Schleswig. But certain damploving groups disappear from alfalfa in Hungary, for example Hydrophilidae and Staphylinidae. Coccinellidae, Curculionidae and various saprophagous forms (Phalacrididae, Cryptophagidae, Lathrididae) remain about the same. Spiders, and especially ants, are found in much greater numbers in Hungary.

Fauna of alfalfa in Hungary

On the ground are to be found the saprophagous forms *Cryptophagus punctipennis*, *Enicmus transversalis*, *Melanophthalma transversalis*, and carnivores such as *Calathus ambiguus* and *Microlestes maurus;* among the plants phytophagous forms such as *Apion aestimatum* (258 out of the 314 plant-feeders collected), and predators such as *Halyzia*. Among the Hemiptera the most important are *Adelphocoris lineatus* and *Lygus campestris*. The ants, as we have seen, are very abundant, especially *Myrmica ruginodis*, which follows *Formica rufibarbis* and *Leptothorax tuberum*. As for the larvae of insects, it is no longer those of weevils that are most numerous, as it is in Schleswig and the region round Paris: here the caterpillars of Lepidoptera make up half of the insect larvae, those of *Phytodecta* 16%, and those of Coccinellidae 17%. The very numerous aphids belong to a species (*Therioaphis ononidis*) which is not found in our fields in France.

Seasonal variations in Hungary

May. Many aphids in the vegetational layer, along with caterpillars and *Phytodecta*. *Myrmica* abounds on the ground along with Staphylinidae, small Carabidae and saprophagous forms such as *Cryptophagus*, *Enicmus* and *Melanophthalmus*.

June. Carnivorous and saprophagous forms decrease on the ground as well as among the plants. Aphids disappear. Hereafter, on the ground, *Formica* accompanies *Myrmica*. Plant-feeders get ahead of carnivorous and saprophagous forms.

July. Strong build-up of aphids, along with their predators, the larvae of Syrphid flies and of Coccinellid beetles. *Formica* remains strong on the ground.

August. Sharp fall in numbers of phytophagous larvae in among the plants, and also of ants. Aphids diminish greatly, then disappear. The carnivores and detritus-feeders reappear.

September. The vegetation dies back almost completely. *Myrmica* and *Formica* are found together on the ground.

In the Mediterranean Region the differences become still more marked. For example in the list of 160 insects given by Giunchi as frequenting alfalfa in Italy, only about thirty are found in West Germany. The Orthoptera, Lepidoptera, Chrysomelid and Lamellicorn beetles, and the ants increase much more than they do further north, but, on the other hand, the carnivores are very similar in number to those in Schleswig.

Another ecological catastrophe: insecticidal treatment

Although we shall be going more deeply into the matter of insecticides in the final chapter of this book, it is possibly of interest to speak at this point about the effects of insecticidal treatment in the special case of an alfalfa crop

Boness compared with a great deal of care the state of the fauna before and after treatment with toxaphene, an insecticide that is persistent but not very toxic. After five to ten days the population declines, but after four to six weeks it can be considered that the losses have been completely made good. If at this point a second treatment is given, then the subsequent recovery is slower and less complete; but this may possibly be accounted for merely by the passing of the season. The damage to insects living on the ground is never as great as that among the plants, and is to some extent dependent on rain, which washes a certain amount of the toxic chemical down on to the soil.

Among the plants the reduction of the population, which reaches 50 %, is accounted for largely by the larvae of thrips, but hardly by their adults. The aphids, the larvae of *Apion*, of Cecidomyidae and of *Meligethes*, do not suffer much. As the use of Moericke traps enables us to demonstrate, the devastated zone is recolonised by insects flying in from surrounding areas. The spiders living among the plants are more or less completely killed off by the insecticide, but on the ground they can survive very well. The mites among the plants fall by as much as 75 %, but quickly return to normal; those of the ground level are hardly affected. The Collembola both on the plants and on the ground are almost annihilated. Psocoptera such as *Lachesilla pedicularis* develop normally, or so it seems, in hay-cocks treated with toxaphene. Thrips lose 50–90 % of their young stages, but after two to four weeks a return to normal is brought about by thrips flying in from untreated zones. The Heteroptera, and more especially the Miridae, lose 50–75 %, and then quickly return to normal; Homoptera are not affected. The beetles of the plant layer are particularly sensitive, and their numbers may drop by 95 %, but those on the ground do not suffer. The parasitic Hymenoptera are strongly affected only among the plants, and so are the Diptera. The big Diptera, strong fliers such as *Hydrellia*, Agromyzids and *Oscinella* hardly suffer, no doubt because their robust wings allow them to take to the air quickly when spraying begins.

Naturally, this picture of the toxicity of toxaphene can change quickly under different meteorological conditions: toxaphene is active only above 16°C, and we have already seen the effect of rain, which can wash the insecticide down on to the surface of the soil. This effect naturally varies according to the properties of the chemicals, some of which are far more lethal than toxaphene, but less persistent. Since certain chemicals, for example 'systemics', are strongly selective, we have the power to release among the alfalfa quite local blitzes, and this opens up some very interesting possibilities for experimental synecology.

How does the field of alfalfa differ from other fields? This question deserves to be asked of the synecological set-up, because we have noted very clearly that a large number of the insects listed above are not specially associated with alfalfa. In a general way there is a sort of faunistic ocean, more or less uniform, in which the cultivated fields represent islands; they are not really islands, but rather reefs that the waves may wash over almost completely.

For a start, a comparison can be made with a related leguminous crop, clover. What differences are there between a field of alfalfa and a field of clover? There are few well-marked differences, indeed half of the insect species are the same. All the same, it is curious to note that the alfalfa has more affinity with insect associations typical of drier areas, whereas clover has insects allied to those of more humid grasslands. For example the genus *Amara*, a Carabid beetle that likes sun and dry conditions, is found in large numbers on the soil of the alfalfa field. On the soil of the clover field there are fewer leaf-hoppers, more Carabidae, fewer Staphylinidae, more Gamasid mites. In the plant layer of the clover there are fewer aphids, fewer nematocerous flies, more brachycerous flies. As far as the ground-living forms are concerned, the differences between the edges and the middle of the field are more pronounced among the woodlice and Collembola, which are much more numerous at the edges. In the vegetational layer the Heteroptera are much more numerous at the edges than they are in the alfalfa field, and so are the leaf-hoppers and adult beetles. Aphids, however, are less numerous at the edges of the field than in the field of alfalfa.

A comparison can also be made with open grassland, but this is more tricky because of a great many factors: the plant-cover is much more mixed, lasts much longer, and covers the ground much more fully than do either the alfalfa or the clover. Certain species such as *Nebria brevicollis* are hardly ever found except in alfalfa or clover, not in grassland. Homoptera, Heteroptera, Psyllidae and grasshoppers are much more numerous in all kinds of grassland than they are in either alfalfa or clover.

Other kinds of cultivated fields

In this connection it would have been interesting if we had had time to go into similar detail about the insect fauna of fields of potatoes, rye, or beetroot, which has been so well studied by the Germans, but this would take too long. A few points about a field of *rye*, investigated by Heydemann, may be noted.

In this case the nature of the soil, whether heavy or light, is very important to the insect fauna. The author made an interesting observation in relation to a narrow sandy strip of about 300 square metres situated in the middle of a field of heavy soil; certain species, such as *Carabus auratus*, never penetrated at all into the sandy area. This is all the more surprising since we are talking about *cursorial* insects, which move relatively quickly. How are they able to appreciate the sudden change in the nature of the soil, or of the microclimate above it, without ever making a mistake? On the other hand Heydemann also found great differences between the edges and the interior of his field, but now the difference was the opposite of that in the field of alfalfa; the insects were *much more numerous in the middle of the field*.

Within the *potato field* Heydemann was especially struck to note how poor was the insect fauna compared with that of the adjoining land, which was sandy: a maximum of 450 individual insects per square metre compared with 750 outside. In addition there was a characteristic difference between the ridges and the furrows, since the furrows were moister and more sheltered from the wind; their fauna was 10–20 % greater than that of the ridges. Climatic conditions in a potato field are extreme, and semi-desert. It is not

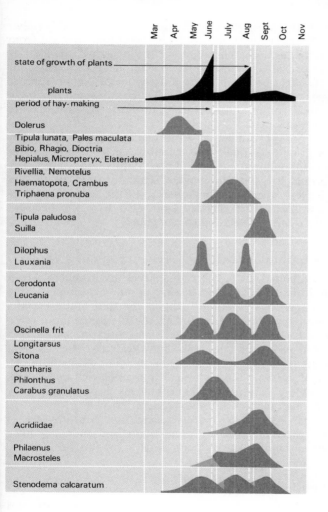

Figure 43. The abundance of insects living in a meadow, shown in relation to two periods of hay-making. The pale green areas indicate periods when the insects are present as larvae (after Boness, 1953).

171

surprising to find that the edges of the field are considerably richer in numbers, brought about no doubt by continual straying from the surrounding land. The nature of the soil, whether it is light or heavy, is also of primary importance, but in unexpected ways, for instance in its effect on the nocturnal activities of certain species. Generally speaking, the link between soil conditions and the insect fauna is much more important than was realised before Heydemann's work.

The field of *beetroot* studied by Prilop has relatively little vegetable debris lying on the ground, and therefore has few saprophagous insects, but many predators, Carabid and Staphylinid beetles. The dominant beetles are Cryptophagidae. There are masses of flies among the leaves, especially Nematocera. All the same, according to Prilop, few species are directly associated with the beetroot except *Atomaria linearis* and *Blitophaga opaca*.

A different biological setting – synecology in a forest

Besides the cultivated crop, there is another environment which offers, with little trouble, that dream of the synecologist, the perfectly homogeneous vegetation; this is the tree, and especially the assembly of trees into a forest. This ideal is much more often approached in forest than in grasslands, and everyone knows that there are forests of firs, beeches, oaks and chestnuts, often of great extent. In strict truth, it is in the *tree top zone* that uniformity is to be found; on the ground the undergrowth is often rich and varied. And unfortunately the treetops have scarcely been explored by ecologists, through lack of suitable ladders.

All the same, because of the ever-increasing consumption of wood for industrial purposes, a great many entomologists have studied forest entomology.

Predators and parasites

The most interesting, and most original discoveries of these last few years (1957–64), in my opinion at least, are to be found in a stimulating memoir by L. Tinbergen (brother of the well-known ethologist Niko Tinbergen) and in a collective work edited by Morris (1963) the great specialist on forest entomology in Canada.

For more than ten years Tinbergen studied a pine-wood that he had known when he was a child, and of which he knew the bird-population very well. Among the birds was *Parus major*, which fed on pine caterpillars and Tinbergen began by estimating the density of these by taking a great many sample twigs and counting the larvae that were feeding on them. At the same time he counted their droppings, which he caught on cloths spread out underneath the trees; the shape of the dropping enabled him even to distinguish the species of the caterpillars, among the three or four that concerned him. The wood was divided into sections, and the density of the birds estimated from the dawn chorus. In order to find out what the birds ate he had to resort to keeping them in nesting-boxes.

The percentage of captures of different species of insect varies considerably. An *index of risk* (R) can be calculated $N_a = R_A D_A t$, where D_A is the density of the predators of species A during the period t, and these pursue prey N of species a. There is a strong correlation between the risk and the size of the prey, which depends to some extent on the fact that the bird does not like certain kinds of caterpillar, and that several kinds are inedible. Tinbergen did not find any clear correlation between the index of risk and cryptic or concealing coloration, though the risk did seem a little less for insects with this type of coloration. But above all, *when a new species of prey made its first appearance, its index of risk was at first very low, but then rose sharply.*

Tinbergen admits that the birds adopt a pursuit technique especially for this new prey ('specific searching image'). Both birds of a pair begin to catch a lot of the new prey at about the same time, as if the first of the two to learn how to catch it had taught the right technique to the other. This is quite a likely hypothesis because, on the one hand a pair of birds often hunt together, and on the other de Ruiter has shown that jays which are offered a particular species of caterpillar find it much more easily after the first time.

Mook, Mook and Heitrens (1960), moreover confirm this speculation of Tinbergen, and have clearly shown that *Parus major* learns to catch *Bupalus pinarius*. Here, then, is one factor which mathematical ecologists have not yet, and justifiably, been able to take into account in the calculations. In these circumstances, following I know not what chimera, Tinbergen and Klomp try to show that what they have observed conforms with Nicholson's curves of the oscillation in numbers of predators and prey. Nicholson assumed – and has been much criticised for doing so – that the host had a constant capacity for multiplication, a constant and simple technique so far as it applies to the parasite or the predator, and to the oscillations of the rate of growth of population resulting from these factors. Now Tinbergen and Klomp showed that the area of pursuit decreases with the density of the prey, that a parasite has a limited number of eggs, and even that each time an insect oviposits this puts a temporary inhibition on the next egg-laying; whereas Nicholson did not accept any limit on the fecundity of the parasite, and assumed the vigour of the pursuit was independent of the distribution of the prey.

Klomp's work dealt only with insects, but we have come up against additional difficulties in studying predation in birds. Pirop (1960) studied more closely the attitude of larvae of the Tenebrionid beetles *Diprion* and *Neodiprion* when a bird came near; they took up a twisted attitude which seemed to make a bird, or even an insect parasite, hesitate. The Hymenopteron *Exenteros*, which parasitises these larvae, seem always to be taken in by this, and this actually reduces its rate of reproduction. But Ichneumon and Tachinid parasites in the presence of these larvae show an adaptive behaviour which avoids exciting this intimidating attitude by the larva.

All these factors, without counting those that we still do not know about, combine to discourage the premature application of mathematics to the ecology of the open air. Besides, Morris (1959) had hardly any more success when he tried to apply Nicholson's formulae to two sawflies on thorn. Huffaker (1958), noted that size, as well as the number of crevices in the substratum, providing possible hiding-places, had enormous effect on the equilibrium between parasite and prey.

This study of the effect of birds, of disease, and of insecticides on the insect populations of forests was set out in a series of memoirs edited by Morris. We cannot even summarise this masterly work, which puts the Canadian forest entomologist far ahead of the rest of the world. We must mention here one odd piece of work, which concerns itself with *the effect of spiders on the insect fauna*, an aspect very important, and very little understood. (Loughton, Derry and West, 1963.)

This concerns, once again, the autecology of *Choristoneura fumiferana*, that insect which does so much damage to Canadian fir-trees. Do spiders trap this sawfly or do they not? We do not know anything for certain, but it seems likely that web-building spiders mostly catch flying insects, and almost never insects that run or climb, and it would seem that the predatory spiders which attack insects harmful to crops are predominantly web-builders. The population of predatory spiders has been estimated at from 1,100–7,500 per acre of forest. Vite and Turnbull agree that spiders feed on the most abundant insects, without discrimination, that is to say that what they catch is determined by chance. By enclosing the twigs on which occur the spiders that attack these sawflies it is possible to collect from $2 \cdot 65 - 2 \cdot 34$ for every ten square feet of foliage. Now to measure the degree of predation, the authors used a *serological method*. Rabbits were injected with serum prepared from the sawflies, and serum from the rabbits was used in precipitin tests with extract from the intestine of the spider. Notwithstanding certain limitations, the test seems reliable. From this it is deduced that sawflies are mainly caught by Thomisid spiders, along with some Salticids and Micryphantids. The percentage of spiders that had fed on sawflies ranged from 6 to 20%, and followed the fluctuations of the sawfly population.

Field and forest

In a piece of work that is already getting old (Chauvin, 1948) I asked myself how far the fauna of a cultivated field differed from that of the faunistic ocean in which it stood. This is a very tricky question, because synecological studies have hardly been pushed far enough to allow detailed comparisons to be made. Tischler (1958) nevertheless tried to compare the fauna of fields with that of the neighbouring woods, and was able to draw a number of exact deductions. He principally used Barber traps. In woods and shrubberies the number of species caught was very great; they were overwhelmingly spiders, *Opilion*, Silphid beetles, ants and scorpionflies, and of these a much greater variety was found than in a cultivated field. The latter, however, held a much greater number of Chrysomelid beetles, and moreover each species was represented by more individuals than in the woods.

There is evidence of many cases of substitution, or vicariousness, where one species in the wood is replaced by a related, but distinct species in the field, and *vice versa*.

The population maximum in the cultivated field comes in summer, from May to August, but in the wood the maximum comes at the end of summer and in winter. The hedgerows, and especially the *margins of woods* provide a place for hibernation, and the species of the edges of woods are surprisingly numerous in comparison with those of the field, or even of the interior of the wood. All the same at harvest-time the species driven out of the fields do not seek shelter at the edges of woods, but in adjoining fields. One part of the fauna of grain-crops moves in this way to colza, either by flying or by walking. Scherney (1953) therefore marked Carabid beetles (*Carabus*, and *Pterostichus vulgaris*) and showed that they migrated up to 200 metres in a few weeks. Skhuravi found a Pterostichus capable of moving 75 metres in ten days.

To conclude: *the practice of cultivation brings about a great disturbance of the insect environment, and impoverishes the fauna.*

The true significance of variations of population within the forest

The splendid studies of Morris and his co-workers on the fauna of the fir forests of Canada are too many, and even more they are developing too quickly, for us to be able to summarise them here. All the same, one ought to mention one set of ideas which analyse very minutely the notion of 'mortality', entirely in relation to the sawflies of fir-trees. The true significance of a 'mortality factor' is difficult to assess in practice: it depends not only on what fraction of the population it is possible to destroy, but still more on what fraction can be destroyed in isolation, because this destruction is added to the other factors that determine the balance of population of the species concerned. Balch and Bird showed this well by introducing into their calculations an 'index of tendency', expressed as the population of one year divided by the population of the previous year. It is then possible to detect even very small changes in the population. For instance, a mortality of 97% maintained a stable population of *Diprion*, with an index of tendency therefore 100; if the mortality fell to 95%, then the index of tendency rose to 200; but if the mortality rose to 99% then the index of tendency fell to 20, and the population collapsed.

Morris and other authors proposed to go further, and to compile mortality tables for insects on the lines of those existing for human populations. He adds, rightly enough, that what matters in nature is not to know if a given species has a regular mortality of 10% or of 90%, because this gives a clue only to the potential rate of growth of the population, and not to what happens during outbreaks. What are important are the small variations of mortality here and there from the normal, the consequences of which are shown by the index of tendency. In the same way, the effect of meteorological factors may be applied, not through climatic catastrophes which can be easily recorded, but by the prolonged effect of small variations that are not lethal in themselves, but which are difficult either to detect or to interpret. However, this is what

Greenbank (1956) has tried to do.

The mortality may change, too, according to the age of the population, which means that a given population level does not signify much by itself: it may be attained by one population in full growth, and by another in the course of its decline. On the other hand, Cole drew attention to the small variations, quite incapable by themselves of producing any important effect in one generation, but the effects of which could accumulate over several generations. If, for example, the mortality of the pine sawfly falls to 95 %, this means a strong probability of an outbreak if it continues for five years. Some authors have tried to measure in the laboratory what is the 'normal' mortality of the species, in the absence of parasites, disease, or unfavourable weather, but it is difficult to see how such results could be applied in nature.

Some other observations by Wellington (1957), which will without question become famous, show clearly that a population may not remain the same after an outbreak as it was before. This author studied *Malacosoma pluviale*, classifying the larvae according to their phototropism in the laboratory. He distinguished larvae of Type I, which were very active, and turned towards the light almost at once; and those of Type II, which remained in a heap, and turned towards the light only a little, or not at all. Now there are important correlations between this simple test and various biological idiosyncrasies. The general activity of larvae of Type I is greater, and their development is faster; they are less liable to infection, because they move about, and do not remain in contact with each other's excrement; and they can easily be recognised in nature from the fact that their cocoons are elongate, whereas those of Type II are very much crumpled. Type I predominates at the beginning of invasions. Wellington was able to eliminate the hypothesis of some disease that exclusively attacked Type II; it is simply a matter of differences of behaviour which seem to be hereditary. Towards the end of an outbreak the cocoons are almost all of Type II, and their inhabitants are sometimes so feeble that they cannot maintain themselves even under favourable conditions.

In 1960 Wellington mixed the two types of caterpillar in varying proportions, and the difference in the cocoon identified them as belonging to one type or the other, in the correct proportions.

In this instance, therefore, the mere population density means nothing unless it is known which type is concerned. It may be added that Wellington, by simple experiments in tropism, has shown similar disparities in other insects.

The fauna of the treetops

There has been little research into the fauna of the crowns of big trees, for obvious practical reasons. However, the bioclimatic conditions up there are so different from those close to the ground that the associated fauna should show very different characteristics. According to Horegott (1960), in East Saxony, 42% of the fauna of the crown of *Pinus silvestris* consists of spiders, 11% are beetles and bugs. There are also a very great number of Collembola, some of which are not found anywhere else. Among spiders the Araneidae, Thomisidae, Theriidae and Salticidae predominate; among beetles it is the Curculionidae and Coccinellidae; among Heteroptera, the Miridae.

Lepointe (1964) studied resinous trees such as juniper and cypress to find what sort of fauna they had in summer and winter. His conclusions, many of them new, are difficult to summarise in a few words. Sometimes the insects were relatively more numerous when the humidity was high (the hygrophile fauna of the cypress); sometimes, on the contrary their abundance is related inversely to the humidity (the xerophile fauna of the juniper). This difference is especially linked with the physical properties of the branches: their density, and their powers of losing water by evaporation, or of absorbing or losing heat. With the help of very simple experiments, of a kind that might be called 'experimental ecology', Lepointe tested the effects of various factors on the insect fauna: humidity and rain – by watering; sunlight – by putting the tree into shade, or alternately by directing sunlight on to the tree with mirrors; and wind – by screens. It is the structure of the tree that is important, and also whether the branches are green or dry, because death, followed by desiccation, seriously alters the physical properties of the plant.

Important movements of the insect population take place up and down the trunk, from the ground to the foliage, and *vice versa*. A sticky band round the trunk greatly reduces the number of insects in the foliage, even of some like the Diptera which have wings, but, strangely enough, climb up the trunk instead of flying.

Lepointe's work is very original, and introduces many innovations into methods of studying the fauna of trees.

How insects move about

As in other sections of this book, it is not the intention here to review insect migration in general, but merely to deal with a few phenomena, recently studied, which are relevant to the distribution of insects within the limited environments that particularly interest us, notably cultivated fields and forests. For the rest, there is an excellent review of insect migration and dispersal by Schneider (1962).

Micromigrations

One thing that seems of first rate importance to me, and yet one of the least studied in any methodical way, is the *mean area of displacement* of insects. In the vast majority of instances we do not know whether the insects in a cultivated field, for example, can move through distances measured in tens or in hundreds of metres. How then can problems of equilibrium in insect populations be seriously discussed? Here is one major source of error in calculations.

Several workers have tried to determine this area of displacement, especially by means of *radioisotopes*: Gillies (1961) on

Figure 44. The dominant species of
insects in a potato-field in each
of the months June–September
(after Skuhravy and Novak, 1957).

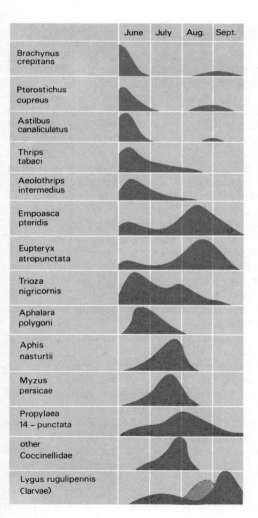

Anopheles gambiae, which moves less than one mile; Goodwin, Jaynes and Davis (1957) on *Pissodes strobi*, which moves a very long way in flight; Baldwin, Riordan and Smith (1958) using radioactive *Melanoplus*, which hardly move more than 30 metres in three weeks if there is plenty of food, but cover 240 metres in six days over bare ground – in that case apparently entirely at random; Green, Baldwin and Sullivan (1957) on *Rhyacionia buoliana*, using radioactive cobalt; Soria and Cline (1961) on *Ceratitis capitata*, of which the males could cover 460 metres in one day, and two individuals achieved 610 metres in 5–7 days.

Roer (1959) put into practice an interesting marking technique with caterpillars of *Pieris brassicae*, in which he made them ingest a neutral red pigment with their food. The colour was ultimately passed on to the adults, and thus indicated where they came from. In general the males stayed close to the place where they hatched from the egg, and it was the females that migrated.

Bailey, Eliason and Iltes (1962) marked mosquitoes by dusting them with a powder of zinc sulphide, which is strongly fluor-escent, and so makes it easy to pick up the insects in ultra-violet light. Another method is to feed *Culex terralis* with sugar-water coloured with a derivative of rhevamine, when they can be detected by means of their coloured excreta.

Joyce and Roberts (1959) made a most curious observation; that the yield of a field that had *not* been treated with insecticide went up when neighbouring fields were treated, even if there was no question of the wind having spread some of the insecticide into it. Consequently it has to be admitted that insects had moved off it into the area that had been cleared of insects by the spraying. The particular example concerned a field of cotton, and the authors stated that although in the untreated field the density of *Empoasca* and of pink boll worms was not altered, on the other hand the number of *Hircothrips* fell. Two fields must be separated by at least 150 metres before one can be treated without the risk of affecting the other.

Now is there not here the principle for a new kind of ecological

Figure 45. The air has its plankton like that of the sea. Relative abundance of various insects and their distribution by height (after Glick in Lindruth, 1949).

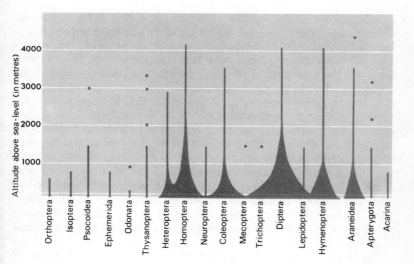

experiment, which would make possible very precise studies of either active or passive micromigration? Moreover in the case of *Hircothrips*, the implications of the experiments of Joyce and Roberts are quite extraordinary: if it is assumed that the thrips are dispersed passively by air-currents it is not reasonable to expect that they would necessarily drift towards an area depopulated by insecticide; and if their migration is an active one, how do they become aware that an empty space is waiting?

A piece of work by Fleschner (1950) tried to establish the *mean distance* that a predator needed to cover to have a statistical chance of getting enough food to complete its development. Among the larvae of three predators of *Paratetranychus citri*: *Stethorus picipes* (Coccinellidae) in one hour searched over forty-eight square inches; *Conventizia hazeni* twenty-six; and *Chrysopa california* 107. During the same period the prey wandered over 357 square inches. Now one prey per square inch is enough for

Stethorus to complete its development, and one every twenty-six square inches for *Chrysopa*. These are data obtained in the laboratory, which need to be confirmed by work in the field. These form part of those exact quantitative measurements that are so sadly lacking, though this does not prevent mathematicians from assuming that the problem is solved.

It is particularly important to determine the 'average scatter' for certain species of Lepidoptera, which do not seem to deposit their eggs on the plants with as much precision as used to be thought. According to Dethier (1959) it is often necessary for the larvae to be able to search actively for their food over a strip 50 cm wide. If they are further than this from suitable food, then mortality may reach 80% or more. Moreover, their sense organs seem to be poor, and they appear to find their food by chance; so much so that Dethier avers that if insects build up in a cultivated field this is not because the food is abundant, but because the plants are close together.

From the work of Henson (1959) it seems that two types of insects can be distinguished: those which go on increasing indefinitely in one place, and end up by devastating it and quickly exhausting their food supply; and others which change their behaviour when they begin to be over-crowded. The latter are able to exploit a source of food without exhausting it, and Henson gives an interesting statistical technique by which the 'aggregation level' can be assessed.

The measurement of 'intensity of assembly' has interested mathematical students of populations for a long time. Waters (1959) discusses the statistical techniques. *Even in the laboratory, in the Tribolium jar* it must not be thought that the insects do not move about, and zoosociologists who are making studies of such populations by taking samples of the flour must allow for this fact. For instance, in a jar of rice bran in which *Ephestia cautella* is being reared, all the young larvae remain in the upper levels of the food material, and it is only from the third stage on that they go down to middle and lower layers. As the density of the insects is increased, the number of individuals in these two lower layers becomes appreciable. On the other hand, the larvae when they are ready to pupate climb up to the top (Takahashi, 1961).

Two authors have done better, and tried to measure experimentally the extent of the dispersion in the laboratory. Naylor (1959–61) tried it on *Tribolium confusum*. His technique consisted in rearing *Tribolium* in flour in circular boxes fitted with a rotating lid with an opening, through which the grouping of the insects could be observed. When the density was low the adults showed some tendency to gather together into groups, but at moderate or high densities this attraction disappeared, and the population spread itself uniformly. But if a note was taken of the sex of the beetles it became apparent that the males had a tendency to form groups, and the females to remain isolated. The author was able to establish that the smell of other beetles, and especially that of males, repelled the female, whereas the males were attracted by the smell of other beetles, and especially that of the females.

Narise and Hiraizumi (1958) placed *Drosophila melanogaster* under similar conditions, in a system of vials which communicated with each other by tubes. At first the movement seen was random, then a mass migration occurred when the population in one of the vials became too dense. From one cause or another the intensity of the migration varied between 2 and 14%, and so did the minimum critical density. Such experiments seem likely to be a fruitful source of ideas for both geneticists and ecologists.

5 The fauna of the soil

Fields and forests are not the only possible environments for insects; others are water, especially fresh water – which is not of particular interest to us in this book, because we are concerned with problems of insect populations – and most of all *the soil*. (Up to the present the insects in fresh water have not been the subject of population studies.)

The organic matter that is to be found so abundantly in the superficial layers of the soil shelters an extremely rich fauna of insects, which at the same time is very specialised, at the mercy of a number of agricultural and climatic influences. Since this population is related to the formation of humus, which is of paramount importance to everyone who cultivates the land, it is attracting more and more attention from biologists. Moreover, although this book is concerned with insects, it is convenient not to ignore other invertebrates, which play an essential part in the ecology of the soil.

The constituents of the soil are the subject matter of a specialised science, *pedology*, but it is not one that we can discuss in any detail here. It should be noted that the soil comprises a mineral component – which, though most important, does not concern us in this book – and an organic component, constantly being added to, and on which the fauna depends. It is this component which is the main source of certain elements essential to plants, notably ammonium nitrate, nitric acid, and part of their phosphorus, sulphur and other inorganic elements. The organic part of the soil has also important physicochemical and even mechanical properties. It is the organic matter in the soil, which gives it cohesion, enables it to retain water, in fact is responsible for a great part of its structure. For all that, the organic component is not very great, only about 7% of a dry soil, whereas air and water make up about 50% of normal soil.

In addition there is a vegetable layer lying on top of the soil. This is of varying thickness and consists largely of plant material in process of decomposition. The study of the soil often involves this layer as well.

The importance of the soil fauna

It is instructive to assess this fauna in terms of biomass, that is to estimate the solid weight of living material which can exist in the soil per unit of surface area; one hectare, for example. The figures reached are astounding. According to Weis Fogh (1948) an average soil in Europe contains 115,500 kilograms dry weight of organic matter per hectare, of which

  6,368 kg are living organisms

  11,550 kg are roots of plants

97,582 kg are inert organic matter, plant debris, dead animals, colloidal matter and humus. It is odd to find that the weight of living animals is more than half as great as the weight of roots.

And now we must go into further detail, since the type of fauna is greatly dependent on the structure of the soil.

Soil structure and fauna

According to Hubiema every type of soil possesses not only a definite composition in terms of organic and colloidal constituents, but also an individual microstructure derived from that composition. For example, soils are more or less porous, but no type exists that is not honeycombed with cavities of varying size. Hubiema estimates that these spaces may occupy 75% of the total volume of the loosest of soils, and about 35% of the most compact. These pores are filled with air or water, and offer all sorts of chances of survival, at least to the microfauna.

It is necessary, in fact, to distinguish between two different types of soil animals, which moreover are to be found in very different ecological conditions. One group, the microfauna, are hardly bigger than one millimetre, or even a fraction of a millimetre. It is these which live in those micropores that have just been mentioned. The members of the macrofauna are far too big for this – for example worms and fossorial insects – and they dig their own burrows, voluminous, and often deep. The air and moisture that they find are sufficient for their needs, and they seem to depend little on the microstructure of the soil, which in any case they themselves modify, often considerably.

Finally, certain authors have wished to distinguish a 'meso-fauna', made up of animals bigger than those of the microfauna, and yet not elongate and worm-like as are the diggers of tunnels. The animals of the mesofauna, on the contrary, tend to surround themselves with a more or less thick carapace, like that of the mites.

Water-dwellers (hydrobionts) and air-dwellers (aerobionts)

In reality, as I said before, the cavities in the soil are not empty, but are filled either with air or with water. So we must make yet another distinction, between animals living in water-filled pores (hydrobionts) and those living in pores filled with air (aerobionts).

The *hydrobionts* do not include many insects, but comprise almost all the microfauna, Protozoa, Nematodes and so on. Furthermore these animals, if conditions become unfavourable, can either encyst themselves in a thick carapace, or quite simply allow themselves to dry up and remain indefinitely in a state of *anabiosis*, or very much retarded development. All these hydro-bionts are doubtless of fresh-water origin, and became dwellers in small cavities by means of a series of adaptations that have favoured becoming smaller and smaller. This small size also helps in their dispersal by all sorts of mechanical means, such as the wind.

The hydrobionts of the soil can be compared with the hydro-bionts that live in mosses, and have similar ecological adaptations.

The *aerobionts* make use of the bigger soil-cavities, since the smaller are generally full of water. That is why care must be used in interpreting figures that claim to express the quantity of a gas that the soil can hold. As Bessard said, 'even with a high porosity, a soil with fine pores which retains a great amount of capillary water will be a relatively deaerated soil, and one poor in water vapour, whereas a soil with a more lumpy structure provides pores of a greater volume, and makes possible an aerial life within the soil. Moreover, contrary to what one might think, the proportion of air in the soil is not stable; on the contrary it may undergo considerable and violent changes, for instance after rain, which percolates down into the soil and drives out the air. When this happens, the big holes are filled, but never the tiny ones, which are effectively protected by capillarity, and by the formation of strings of air-bubbles. On the other hand very heavy falls of rain help to renew the air in the soil.

This 'atmosphere of the soil' has very special characteristics. First, its composition. Although the animals at the surface breathe an air that is very little different from the free air above, below a certain depth carbon dioxide reaches impressive proportions, about 10%, while oxygen content may fall to 2%. In addition the relative humidity is very high, between 90 and 100% for the greater part of the year. at least in temperate climates, where at depths of more than 10 cm the soil may be considered to be saturated; except in the arid steppes, where the relative humidity remains at about 50%.

For another thing, darkness is total, and so growth of green algae and any other living organisms that depend upon photosynthesis is entirely suppressed. Temperature fluctuations are greatly smoothed out, and the atmosphere of the soil is still: so much so that the final products of fermentation, such as ammonia and carbon dioxide, stagnate for long periods in the same place since there is nothing but diffusion to make them move away.

The soil animals, even the aerobionts, must thus all be lovers of moisture (hygrophiles), and if drought-loving forms (xerophiles) are found in the soil they are not true soil-dwellers (Bessard). The integument of the hygrophiles is usually thin, making cutaneous respiration easy, and in addition the continual rubbing in the soil wears away the cuticle, quickly eroding away the superficial waxy layer, or epicuticle. On the other hand, some of these animals are able to protect themselves against desiccation by secreting an abundance of mucus. In contrast to the hygrobionts they do not become encysted, nor do they practise anabiosis (revivification). They are always found moving about in the soil, and sometimes take part in extensive migrations.

Ecological factors in the soil

Clearly the water-content of the soil is the most basic ecological factor. The acidity, or pH as it is called, has not as much effect on aerobionts as on hydrobionts. Acidity of the soil affects chiefly the microflora; it is true that often the microfauna feed on the microflora, and consequently an indirect effect of acidity on the animals cannot be neglected.

The chemical composition of the soil must also be taken into account. Saline soils for example, have a limited, but characteristic fauna. The calcium content is also of great importance, apart from the effect that it has on pH. It does not greatly concern us here, because it hardly matters to most insects, but there are many animals, notably earthworms, molluscs and millipedes which cannot do without sufficient calcium.

It is also evident that the *organic content* of the soil is probably the factor of greatest importance to the fauna, because it controls food supply. Obviously the organic matter in the soil is not fixed, but goes through a cycle of successive degradations, ending finally in carbon dioxide plus water. The process of decomposition goes on only slowly in temperate climates: in the soils of tropical Africa, on the contrary, the action of micro-organisms and the process of chemical changes are immensely speeded up by the heat, and the drenching tropical rain quickly leaches out water-soluble substances that might be useful to animal life. Unless the soil is protected by a well-developed vegetation there occurs a terrible process of *lateritisation*: the silicates come up on to the surface, and the soil quickly turns into a very hard, inert, red rock called *laterite*.

Fortunately this does not happen in temperate countries. As Bessard writes: 'there comes into being, alongside these chains of decomposition, a cycle of organic matter in the soil, the course of which is more or less dependent on the type of activity shown by the edaphon, and which is orientated either towards mineralisation or towards humification, these two tendencies being linked together in proportions that are very variable'.

The zoological groups of the soil

As I have already said, although we are concerned here with insects, it is difficult not to say something about other groups of animals that occur in the soil.

We shall pass quickly over the *Protozoa*, which must be very abundant in the soil, but to count them is very difficult. They feed particularly on bacteria, and make up their diet with general detritus, taking bacteria and detritus separately or together. They are affected most of all by the state of aeration and moisture of the soil, but little affected by its pH. They are found most abundantly in the richest soils, for example in gardens.

Among the worms of the soil must be first mentioned the *nematodes*, which may be as many as 20 millions per square metre, and are sometimes numerous enough to do serious damage, for instance in greenhouses. They depend chiefly on organic matter, and therefore are usually found in the upper layers of the soil (according to Bessard, 90% of the worms are to be found in the first five centimetres below the surface). They feed on bacteria, detritus and even on plants. It is among the plant-feeding group of nematodes (especially the Tylenchidae) that the agricultural pests ('eelworms') are found.

But first place among the animals of the soil must be given to earthworms, or lumbricids, which play an absolutely essential part in the breaking down of the organic matter, and which are helped in this by their huge size: more than two metres long in certain tropical species. It is difficult to estimate their numbers with any exactitude, because they seem to be irregularly distributed, massing together in certain places. In grassland, for example, there may be a thousand of them per square metre which works out at 4,000 kilograms of earthworms per hectare, or more than half by weight of the fauna of the soil.

It is known that they come up to feed on vegetable debris on the surface, and take what they have chosen back into the depths, along with some mineral matter. The uncountable 'wormcasts' that are to be seen on the surface are the spirals formed by their excreta, which other species of worms allow to accumulate in their burrows as they move along. The mixing up that goes on in this way is extraordinarily efficient, and in temperate countries may involve as much as twenty or even sixty tons per hectare. According to Kollmansberger (1956), in certain regions of the humid tropics the astronomical figure of 210 tons per hectare is reached! It is said that these animals have attracted the attention of cultivators, to the point where they have decided to set up breeding farms for earthworms. There are cases where the infertility of a piece of ground seems to be entirely due to the lack of earthworms.

The arthropods

Before coming to the insects, which are well represented in the soil, we must first note the occurrence of very many mites. It is in the soil of forests that they are most numerous, and where they reach several hundred thousand individuals per square metre. They are also very abundant in grassland, but soil that has been worked is unfavourable for them, and their numbers drop to 100,000 or even to 20,000 per square metre. Mites are either detritus feeders or carnivores. The very important *Oribates* group, which represents from 40 to 70%, take a very active part in the decomposition of organic vegetable matter in the soil.

The Myriapods (millipedes) are a very mixed group, which is irregularly represented in the soil. Among them the Symphilidae are truly at home in damp, rich soils, with plenty of organic matter;

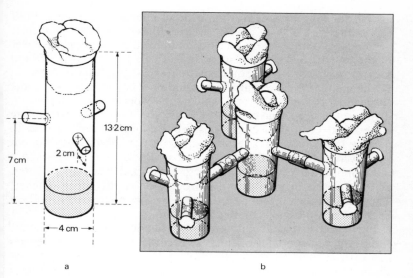

Figure 46. Equipment used to study the 'micromigrations' of *Drosophila*. *a*, the dimensions of an individual population-tube; *b*, a set of four such tubes coupled together, as used in practice (after Sakai, Narisse, Hiraizumi and Iyama).

a

b

5,000 of them per square metre may be found, and their diet is strictly vegetarian. They eat particularly detritus, but some of them may attach themselves to the new tissues of young plants. Other myriapods, *Julus*, live a life very much like that of earthworms, and like them take material from the surface down into the ground.

The insects of the soil

A large number of insects spend part or all of their lives in the soil, but the Collembola must take pride of place, because, along with the mites, they make up 80–90 % of the arthropod fauna of the soil. These are very strange insects in many respects, for one thing in their apparent 'resistance to evolution'. They are a group that has existed for long periods of time without change, and their earliest representatives, 300–400 million years old, hardly differ from their descendants of the present day, except in having two segments fewer in the antennae. The number of individuals is very variable, and may range from a few thousands to 700,000 per square metre, in the debris that is richest in organic matter. They mostly live on the surface of the ground, and only a few species are adapted to living in the deeper layers. Many Collembola are very demanding about their ecological conditions, 'thus confining each species to narrow limits, and as a result producing populations of different composition only small distances apart' (Bessard). Collembola are much more active than many micro-arthropods such as *Oribates*, and their cycle of growth and reproduction is also much quicker. They play a much bigger part than these other micro-arthropods in breaking down organic matter in the soil.

Furthermore it is difficult to describe in a few words what are the food requirements of Collembola, because although each species has a strict diet, all the Collembola taken together will eat anything, so to speak: 'Some prey on nematodes, on rotifers, on other Collembola, and on a diversity of prey; others feed on dead animals; but the great majority take vegetable food. Among the different kinds of food they choose are algae, mycelium and spores of fungi, pollen grains, bacteria, and even the living tissues of tender young plants (Sminthuridae)' (Bessard).

In the soil of tropical countries, however, Collembola yield pride of place to Isoptera, or termites, whose numbers reach fantastic proportions. As Grassé has said: 'In certain parts of Africa it is impossible to drive a pick into the ground anywhere without digging up termites'. The immense termitaria of *Bellicositermes* contain many millions of individuals, which are ceaselessly occupied in turning over soil and vegetable debris. Bessard comments that they cannot be said to play an important part in the formation of humus, because their intestinal symbionts enable them to extract all the organic matter from the wood that they eat. On the other hand they continually turn over the soil and transport

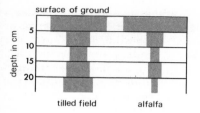

Figure 47. Mites in the soil beneath a crop of alfalfa are more concentrated towards the surface than they are beneath a ploughed field (after Höller, 1956).

the mineral constituents from below to the surface, and *vice versa*, and it is very likely that this action may delay or even prevent the fatal process of lateritisation, which signals the death of the soil.

The termites may be compared with the ants of temperate regions, especially *Formica polyctena*, in their effect on the soil of forests. This species of ant is fossorial, and gathers round its nest a considerable mass of rubbish. On one occasion I measured 250 litres of sand thrown out on to the surface by a single ant colony. The vast pile of twigs from which the nest is built up, and which may be higher than a man, is disturbing to some of the foresters. At the time when we were trying to develop 'ant-farming' to combat some of the insect pests of trees, foresters asked whether the good work that the ants undoubtedly did in this respect was not counterbalanced by their deleterious effect on the formation of humus because of their mania for building. In the end it was felt that this had a negligible effect, and that the small drawbacks of the ants were balanced by their many benefits.

Certain species of Coleoptera frequent the soil, not only as larvae, but throughout their life; certain Carabidae, Pselaphidae, Colydiidae, and Curculionidae, for example. A very large number go into the soil only as larvae, but even then are often harmful to crops, such as the larvae of Elateridae, commonly called wireworms; white-worms, or larvae of chafers; weevil larvae such as *Otiorhynchus, Sitona*, etc. . . . which feed on the root-nodules of leguminous plants. Other beetles, when adult, are carnivorous and seek their prey in the soil: various species of Carabidae, and Staphylinidae, which catch other insects, snails and slugs, or earthworms; tiny species of Staphylinidae, Pselaphidae or Scydmenidae look for prey on their own scale, and find it among the uncountable numbers of micro-arthropods. In addition many adult beetles are detritus-feeders, and find their food within the soil, although mostly in the superficial layers: *Atheta* (Staphylinidae), Liodidae, Trichopterygidae, and many clavicorn beetles such as Lathrididae and Cryptophagidae.

Among Diptera, certain families such as Tipulidae and Bibionidae have larvae that are detritus-feeders. D'Aguilar and Bessard specially studied the action of larvae of Bibionidae in a variety of composts. These larvae are to be found in autumn in masses of 40 to 1,400 individuals all over the forests, and their activity continues almost all winter. They pupate in mid-April, and are adult in May. The larvae in their second instar feed on dead leaves which have already begun to decompose. The intestines of the fly larvae can only incompletely digest all this material, and a high proportion of the vegetable matter is still present in their excreta. All the same the proportion of nitrogen to carbon is distinctly raised in the faeces, especially when the larvae feed on dead oak-leaves. There is thus a definite contribution to the process of humidification.

Larvae of Diptera may total as many as 250–1,000 larvae per square metre.

The fauna of the soil in relation to cultivation

Clearing the ground, and even more, cultivating it, disturbs the previously undisturbed soil, and always tends to impoverish the fauna; but a new fauna becomes established, which is typical of cultivated and manured land, and which may be quite rich and stable, at least to the extent of tolerating the processes of cultivation.

The surface layers are worked over, not only with the plough, but also with rotary machines such as the disc-harrow, which

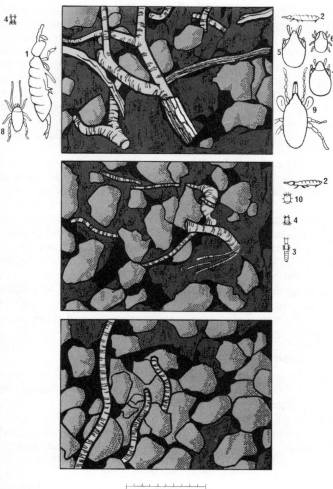

Figure 48. Section through the soil of a Danish meadow at depths of 1 cm, 2½ cm and 4½ cm. In the top two sections will be found: 1, *Isotoma viridis*; 2, *Folsomia quadrioculata*; 3, *Tulbergia krausbaueri*; 4, *Brachychthonius furcillatus*; 5, *Schelovibates laevigatus*; 6, *Tectocepheus velatus*; 7, *Peloptulus phaenotus*; 8, *Empodes berlesa*; 9, *Pergamasus runciger*; 10, *Tarsonemoides belemnitoides* (after Weis Fogh, 1948).

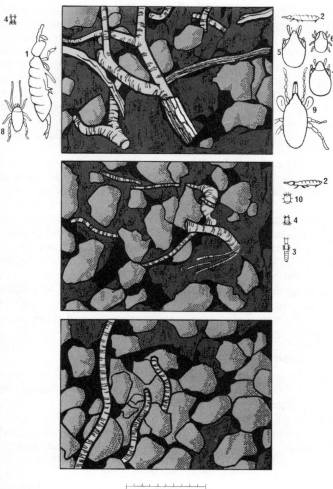

1mm

break up the soil, and thus encourage its rapid colonisation by surface-living species such as Collembola, mites and various species of insects. In contrast *Oribates*, which likes a more stable medium, descends deeper into the soil. Then the rapid evaporation which is caused by the breaking up of the soil is unfavourable to moisture-loving forms, while the disc-harrow mechanically destroys many of the larger forms of life, the worms, the big insects and the millipedes. For reasons that are complex, certain clearly defined species start to increase at a devastating speed; a particular example is the wireworms in grass that is ploughed and sown with crops such as alfalfa and other legumes.

As for the use of fertilisers, I have already had occasion several times to mention their effect on the fauna of the soil. Mineral fertilisers enrich the fauna, for reasons that are poorly understood, but probably by indirect means. The effect of organic manures is easier to understand. These favour the many insects that feed on detritus. Things are not quite so simple, however, and it may happen that some species dwindle or even disappear after manure has been spread, for reasons that the ecologists have not clearly explained. As for the species peculiar to compost-heaps, these will prosper in their special habitat until the decay of the vegetable material has progressed to a later stage, when the specialised forms are driven out, and the normal fauna of the soil takes over.

The part played by animals in the soil

According to Franz the more animals there are in the soil, the more fertile it is and this prompts us to examine more closely the role of these animals, especially in the formation of humus.

The mixture of complex chemical substances which is known collectively as humus is of very great practical importance, and is almost entirely responsible for the growth of the higher plants, yet biologists and pedologists have only paid attention to it in the last twenty years or so. We know, in the words of Bessard, that: 'the formation of humus is almost exclusively the work of *vegetable*

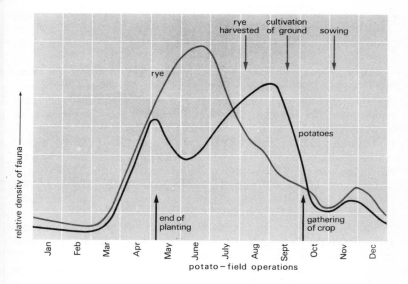

Figure 49. How cultivation of crops affects the insects lying on the surface of the soil. Both in rye (green line) and potatoes (black line) the insects have passed their maximum before the crop is gathered (after Heydemann, 1953).

micro-organisms, the fauna having no more than a catalytic effect. The humus, by its slow release of minerals, a process partly helped along by the animals, is a progressive source of chemical elements that go towards feeding the higher plants. . . . The part played by the animals in the soil is thus fundamental to the mechanical and physical breaking down of the plant-debris, whereas they play only a secondary part in the biochemical processes by which the humus is built up.'

It must be stressed that the function of the animals is a secondary one only in the *biochemical processes* leading to the formation of humus; but that in other ways, perhaps just as important, the role of the animals is fundamental. This is particularly true of the process of *fragmentation* of the vegetable debris into finer and finer particles. This continued fragmentation of the organic matter in the soil enormously increases its surface area, and thereby speeds up still more the biochemical processes that are going on. It is a general rule in chemistry that the finer a solid is powdered, the more quickly it is attacked by any reagent.

A few figures will give an idea of the effect produced by these 'living pestles and mortars', the insects and the other arthropods. After passing through the intestines of earthworms the vegetable debris is hardly bigger than two millimetres; it has been reduced to particles of 30–50 microns by the time it leaves the anus of Collembola, and to only ten microns when passed out by mites. Another way of expressing the result would be to calculate by how much the surface area is increased. The earthworms increase the surface area of the soil particles by no more than 75%, but after treatment by small arthropods such as *Oribates* its surface area has been increased by 500,000%.

Finally, as part of the mechanical effect of the animals in the soil it must not be forgotten that they actively disperse the organic matter both vertically and horizontally, and that this kind of dispersal is almost entirely the work of soil animals. Naturally a good deal of the mineral matter is carried along at the same time. To what extent this goes on has been estimated only for earthworms, where it is said that in ten years the entire humus-layer of a piece of grassland has passed at least once through the intestine of a worm.

Can we completely exclude the soil animals from the biochemical cycle, and confine them to the role of simple browsers and chewers? It seems not, since a distinct increase in the humus content has been found in soil passed by earthworms. This effect is general, but often it does not make its appearance until some time after the faecal pellet has been expelled. The strangest fact about this effect is that it is the work of this or that micro-organism according to the species of arthropod that is being studied. This must mean that the alimentary canal of the animal has a selective effect on the microflora that is different for each species of arthropod, and which favours one element of the microflora, while retarding others.

The consequence of this is that there are particular 'species' of humus, each corresponding to the arthropod fauna that lives in it. According to Kubiena (1953), for example, 'mulch' or soft humus is especially the work of earthworms, whereas a medium humus is generally produced by the action of arthropods. Coarse humus is more often the work of a fungoid mycelium than of animal action. Kubiena has taken these fine distinctions rather far, for example he attributes something between a mulch and a moderate humus to the action of millipedes in the soil.

Insecticides and the soil fauna

In the light of this it is now a good moment to examine the immediate and long-term effects of insecticidal treatments upon the fauna of the soil. These doses of insecticide may be given directly, with the intention of disinfesting the soil or may come about indirectly from spraying of the crops. It can be said that their effects, as far as they are known, are catastrophic to the fauna of the soil, but we are a long way from knowing everything, especially about their long-term effects.

Pesticides may be divided into fungicides, herbicides, vermicides and insecticides. Not only is the chemical composition of all these substances extremely varied, but new ones make their appearance every year. In the majority of cases – and herein lies the drama of chemical warfare, as we shall see later – neither time nor personnel is available to make a study of all the likely consequences of such a treatment, and especially of what any long-term effects might be. All that is known at present, according to d'Aguilar (1964) is that fungicides and herbicides do not appear to have any action, or at least any immediate action, on the fauna of the soil. Vermicides kill all worms without distinguishing the beneficial from the harmful ones. Insecticides, however, are general poisons, harmful not only to insects, but also to earthworms. For instance, according to Goffart (1949), two months after a treatment with parathion not a single earthworm can be found alive in the affected

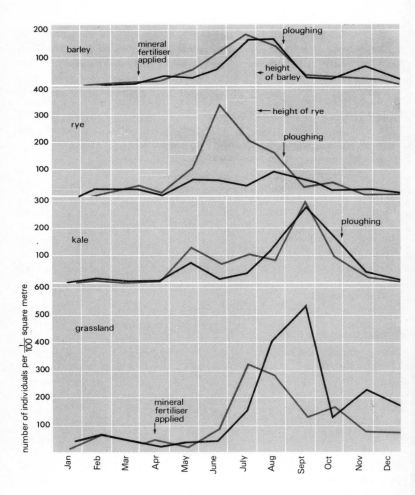

Figure 50. The numbers of Collembola (green lines) and mites (black lines) in the soil reach different levels and in different months, under different crops (after Hammer, 1949).

area. Another substance, sevin, is a powerful killer of earthworms, even in extremely small doses, although it is used as an insecticide.

The most serious aspect of this is that these synthetic insecticides persist so long in the soil, more so than on the surface. This is so for a compound that has now been in use as an insecticide for a long time, benzene hexachloride (hexachlorocyclohexane, or BHC), which is better known than most insecticides for that reason. D'Aguilar took soil from fields that had been treated with BHC several years previously, and placed it in dishes. In every case he found that he could not rear wireworm larvae without a significant mortality, and strangely enough the mortality was greatest in the soil that had been treated longest ago, three years. This raises the question as to what decomposition product of BHC may have been slowly formed, which was even more toxic than the original insecticide. Couturier also recorded a very high mortality among chafer larvae that had emerged from eggs laid in soil one or two years after treatment with BHC.

After treatment with BHC (4–25 kg per hectare) plant-feeding and carnivorous insects declined considerably. Saprophagous insects declined, too, although if the dosage was small they might increase in numbers. On the other hand earthworms and nematodes were not touched, though wireworms and adult Carabid beetles were killed even on the surface of the soil (Grigoreva, 1952). These observations have been taken into greater detail by Sheals (1955). He worked with DDT, BHC and a mixture of DDT + BHC at dosages of 1·350 kg per hectare (at 75–80% of the gamma isomer for the DDT and 13% for the BHC: these isomers are the only active part in the commercial product).

The results may be expressed in table 16 (page 204).

The Collembola that had increased after the use of DDT mostly belonged to the species *Tullbergia crassicuspis*. This curious increase has been compared to the outburst of *Metatetranychus ulmi* on plants that had been dusted with DDT. It will be recalled that Kuene and Hueck think that this increase in populations of mites is due not only to the destruction of predators, but also to a

Table 16 Percentage present after treatment of soil with controls

	Collembola	Mesostigmatid mites	Oribatid mites
Controls	100%	100%	100%
DDT	200	40	40
BHC	40	30	30
BHC + DDT	90	10	10

direct action favouring the production of eggs. We shall see that this favourable action of insecticides to noxious insects, paradoxical though it may seem, is perhaps of general occurrence, if we are to believe Chaboussou, cited in the following chapter.

This favourable action of insecticides on Collembola has been studied. Ehrenhardt, for example, soaked filter-paper in pesticide and placed it in the bottom of a Petri dish; on this was placed soil containing Collembola. Using a number of different toxic compounds, no favourable effect on the Collembola could be detected. D'Aguilar tried to repeat these experiments with *Onychiurnus ghidini*, with the same result: no favourable effect.

Nevertheless this effect exists in nature, though it has never been properly explained. A differential action has been suggested, more rapid on the enemies of the Collembola than on the Collembola themselves. Experiments show, however, that Collembola are strongly sensitive to insecticides. Keller (1951) took many successive samples after a dusting with DDT, and found that although the bulk of the soil fauna disappeared after dusting, local areas were very quickly recolonised from the surrounding areas. Should one say, then, that the rate of recolonisation is greater for Collembola than for other insects? This still cannot be confirmed, though it is known that the rate is different for different species. We don't know very much about it all yet. For example someone must try to estimate the rate of formation of humus following on the application of very small doses of insecticide to the soil, and this has not yet been done.

Here, as in general where the application of insecticides to plants is concerned, we are behaving like the Sorcerer's Apprentice.

Insecticides, or any other chemical substances that are being studied, can be applied with great precision by means of this micro-technique. The operator can not only control the dosage but apply it to any predetermined area of the insect's body.

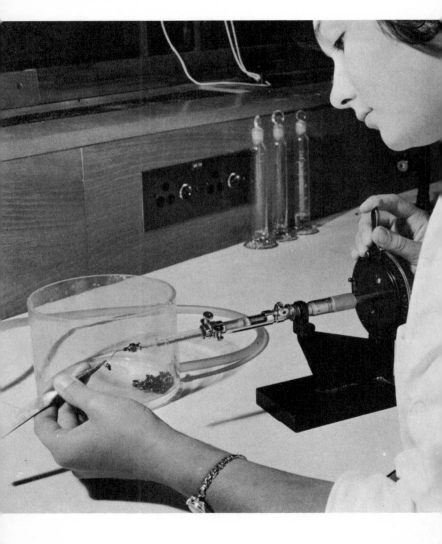

6 The battle against insects

A book about insects as a populace of living animals cannot ignore what is one of their most important characteristics to us: that their interests are often opposed to ours. The man in the street will smile at the idea that a few small insects could be such a terrible menace to man, with all his modern techniques. And yet . . . ! Has he thought of the unwelcome hosts of greenfly, plant-lice and plant-bugs? So what, he says, haven't insecticides, DDT and the rest, done justice to them for a long time now? Certainly not! At one time the problem seemed to be effectively solved, but then *the insects became resistant to insecticides*, in the same way that bacteria become more and more resistant to anti-biotics.

Both are able to do this for the same reason, that they have a tremendous fecundity. They lay so many eggs that some or other of them are bound *to be or to become* resistant to whatever poison is being used against them, and these then become a breeding stock from which arises a strain of the insect or bacterium that is immune to the poison in question. Here the reader must permit me a digression, because it is only with dreadful misgivings that I have written above *to be or to become* resistant.

A digression on the limitations of genetics

Genetics is a very fine science, but, contrary to the claims of certain of its devotees, it does not embrace the whole of biology. We should be suspicious of keys which, according to their inventors, claim to open every door. Often it is just a case of purely verbal explanations, or of assertions that by definition cannot be verified. I should really like to find an example of this among insecticides. As the general public is beginning to realise, many of these are compounds that do not exist in nature, nor ever have existed – they come about only by chemical synthesis, by processes as far removed as possible from what goes on in nature. However, here they are; and the insect's organisation which has never come up against such things in all its 300 million years of evolution, is able in a few months or a few years to develop strains that are resistant to the new compounds. The standard explanation is as follows. If we assume a large enough number of individuals, each laying a great number of eggs, there is always a chance that one of them will undergo a mutation that happens to render it immune to the new poison, and then there is nothing to stop this from fathering a strain.

It will not escape the reader that such an explanation can be applied to anything you like; it could be repeated in any context. It comes back to saying that the chromosomes of insects contain a *preformed answer to every question*, and that this is true not just of one insect, but of all of them, provided that their fecundity is great enough; and not only for the past *but for the future as well*! Put like this, the genetical hypothesis clearly goes too far. As for me, I think that it would be better not to assume in advance that the problem is solved, and to make a serious search for a mechanism by which a resistant strain might *be created*. It is not very likely that the biologists will do this, because, like all men, they prefer an easy explanation! Might there not be an acquired immunity, a 'mithridatisation', involving not only the individual but also the species? This is an accepted phenomenon . . .

The problem of insecticides

This problem of resistance is not the only problem to do with insecticides, but it is the most serious. Resistance is developed, not only among parasites of man, but more or less universally among any insects that are subjected to synthetic poisons regularly and over a long period. The mosquitoes are another, and very important, example of this ability that insects have to evade the traps set by man. Is it possible that malaria may reappear in vast areas from which it was thought to be eradicated? This could in fact happen if the insect vector were to breed there once again in the old numbers.

Examples of this kind of resistance are too numerous to mention, and it is probably a universal phenomenon. Certain classical examples are instructive. The San José Scale, a particularly devastating coccid, has in a few years become resistant to hydro-cyanic acid, one of the strongest toxins. Certain Swedish house-flies, in the town of Arnas, have become so resistant to DDT that doses exceeding two hundred times what is normally lethal do them no harm.

It may be added that resistance to poisons is accompanied by a whole series of physiological modifications – for example, in the case of the flies of Arnas, by the ability to withstand great heat, much greater than normal – but it does not extend to bodily proportions, or to morphological details, which are unaffected.

The empirical way in which insecticides are used, by trial and error, is a serious risk, some of the consequences of which we have already seen in relation to soil insects. The main reason for this attitude seems a difficult one to tackle, because it is commercial. The enormous output of new compounds thrown on to the market each year is far greater than research can cope with. Thus although some of the short term effects are well studied, for instance the question of acute toxicity to mammals, almost nothing is known about the long term effects, and especially of the degree of persis-tence in the soil.

Another thing, all those uncertainties about the methods of sampling insects as used by ecologists, to which I have repeatedly drawn attention, obviously operate equally well on the science of insecticides. For this reason it is a pity that far too many research workers in insecticides are indifferent to, and ignore, the viewpoint of the ecologists. Certainly they acknowledge readily that the progress of insecticidal techniques depends on putting into practice rigorous methods of population sampling; yet when that has been said, they still care very little about making their own contribu-tion to these methods. They are too easily satisfied with the most crude 'counts'.

Most progress has been made in dealing with aphids and scale-insects, but these are the easiest of insects to study, since they

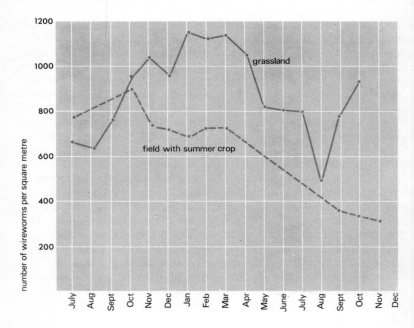

Figure 51. In a field that is ploughed and planted with a summer crop (green line), the number of elaterid larvae (wireworms) is permanently reduced compared with the numbers present in unploughed grassland (black line) (after Cockbill and others, 1957).

move about very little, and so are quite easy to count. The empiricism of the science of insecticides is beautifully illustrated by the researches of Chaboussou, who demonstrated that in certain cases the so-called poisons were actually very beneficial to the insect, improved its metabolism, and increased its fecundity.

Poisonous chemicals and mites

Chaboussou took as an example the multiplication of mites, but there are other comparable examples where insects laid even better after insecticidal treatment. He told me, for instance, of having obtained very large numbers of eggs of *Doryphora*, many more than normal, when the females were fed on potato-leaves that had been dusted with various insecticides. It is only necessary to wait a few days before giving them the leaves to eat; the toxicity has then disappeared, but there remains 'something' on the leaves that not only does no harm to the insects, but is very good for them. One insecticide even greatly facilitates the propagation of an aphid.

Let us leave this, and analyse the phenomenon of 'trophobiosis' as it is called by Chaboussou (I would prefer to call it 'toxotrophy', but let us not squabble about trifles).

1 Do the toxic chemicals have any effect on the plants?
2 Is any such effect good or bad for the insects?

1 As for the first question, a series of 'naïve' observations, carried on over a long period, has given an affirmative answer. First let us say, right away, that the first reassurance that vendors of a pesticide give is that *it is not toxic to plants*; but in this context it must be admitted that in many cases *not only is the plant not injured, but on the contrary it becomes more fleshy and greener*. This has been commented on by all the practical men, but the scientists have not taken an interest in it until recently. And see what Chaboussou found. Vines had been treated with a whole series of insecticides and fungicides (DDT, parathion, sevin, finely divided sulphur) and then the foliage was subjected to various analyses, first for amino-acids, then to a series of tests for total nitrogen, phosphorus, potassium, calcium and magnesium. Then 'among five out of six patches treated with DDT and four out of six treated with phosdrine, the total amino-acids is higher than the average of the controls' (Chaboussou et coll.). 'In regard to potassium, although the differences are not significant (statistically) as they are for amino-acids, nevertheless the greatest increases were found with DDT, while sevin and phosdrine took second place' (ibid.).

In brief, *all these toxins profoundly alter the equilibrium of the plant*. Here the observations of Chaboussou and his colleagues confirm other work such as that of Rodriguez, who found that another insecticide, benzene hexachloride (BHC), profoundly alters the total of nitrogen, potassium and phosphorus in the leaves of haricot beans, of soya, and of cotton. According to the same authors the same is true of leaves of apple-trees treated with DDT, dieldrine and BHC. Even in the absence of direct spraying merely incorporating DDT into the soil increases the total of sugar and of nitrogen in the leaves of haricot and soya beans.

2 *Is the action of insecticides on the plant good or bad for the insects*? Observations of a favourable effect *after* an application are so numerous that it is a mystery why they have not attracted greater and earlier attention from scientists. Undoubtedly this must be put down to the power of preconceived ideas.

It would be tedious to list all the published references. Outbreaks of mites have been noted on apple-trees and nut-trees following upon treatment with DDT, on haricot beans after lindane and malathion, on vines after phosphoric compounds, and so on. ... As Chaboussou said, the peculiarity of these outbreaks is that they affect many species of mites, and a variety of annual and perennial plants, and that they are triggered off by insecticides of quite different chemical composition, not closely related. For example, fungicides, which are developed to attack living organisms as distinct from insects, as are fungi, contribute to outbreaks of red spider mite. Moreover the molecular structure of fungicides has nothing in common with that of insecticides.

This phenomenon is most astonishing, and up to now it has been explained by supposing that the enemies of the mites are more sensitive to the toxic chemicals, and are the first to be destroyed; in particular *Typhlodromus*, the most effective predator of the mites. But according to Rambier, DDT is completely harmless to *Typhlodromus*, and this is the chemical that produces the most violent outbreaks of mites. On the other hand some outbreaks are triggered off quite simply by liberally manuring the soil, which alters the chemical composition of the vegetation; but what harm can this do to the *Typhlodromus*? Moreover some authors are sceptical about the supposed role of *Typhlodromus*, which attacks the mites in the laboratory but hardly ever under natural conditions.

It has also been suggested that the supposed toxins might have a direct action on the mites, increasing their rate of reproduction, but such an effect seems out of the question as far as many insecticides are concerned. Parathion, for instance, is well established as a killer of mites; yet it provokes outbreaks of mites just like other insecticides. This can only be the result of some indirect action, through its effect on the plant.

Since 1948 Chapman and Allen have shown that DDT can act to some extent as a *growth substance* for plants. The favourable effect on the plants can be detected only at certain concentrations. In higher doses the plants become stunted and blackened, exactly as when plant hormones are used in excessive amounts. For the phosphorus insecticides Hascoet thinks that they have a strong and prolonged activating effect on certain plant enzymes such as the peroxidases, and that this can obviously set in motion, step by step, a whole series of metabolic changes.

The explanation for fungicides is more awkward since as Hascoet says: 'at first sight it seems odd that a compound that is essentially toxic to plants – since it has been developed as a fungicide – can have a beneficial effect on the economy of a plant'. All the same, in the case of insecticides containing sulphur, such as captane 'it is possible that the decomposition of the captane involves a liberation of sulphur', which may itself have a beneficial effect on the plant.

In general, as Chaboussou recalls, increasing the nitrogen content is linked with an increase of proteins, and these are substances which are of the greatest importance in the nutrition of all plant-feeders.

This example has been given merely to show at what point the limitations of our knowledge may lead us into the unexpected. Although the science of insecticides has not neglected physiology, it has given altogether too little attention to ecology, and the study of populations. That is why we must now turn to other techniques of insect control, which depend entirely upon things that have been neglected by the insecticide specialists.

Biological control

It is a fine idea to use predatory and parasitic insects to attack other insects that are damaging our crops. This is quite an old idea, and papers about it make up quite a bulky literature (see Balachowsky, 1951). The idea was either to introduce parasites and predators from somewhere else, or to rear in 'insect factories' some of the local parasites that are already present in the right place, but in insufficient numbers. It can be said right away that in a certain number of cases – very few in number – this technique has met with undoubted success, and been very spectacular. This was not because the entomologists who put this technique into operation knew all the details of the biology of parasite and host – this would be pretty well impossible – but quite simply because of good luck. The parasite was so effective, and acclimatised itself so readily, that the scientists needed only to introduce it.

Unhappily events do not always follow so smooth a course, and success and failure are equally difficult to explain. In order to understand them we must return to the study of insect populations, and more especially to the interaction of parasite and prey.

Interaction of parasite and prey

It is impossible here to give even a superficial idea of the innumerable works that have been written about biological control in practice, and even more about biological control in theory. In Utida's laboratory in Japan very profound studies have been carried out on a Pteromalid and a Braconid which attack the Bruchid beetle *Callosobruchus sinensis*. When the three species are mixed in a closed vessel the numbers of the two parasites at first increase rapidly at the expense of their host. The Braconid is most effective in controlling low concentrations of the Bruchid, and the Pteromalid in controlling high ones. Moreover the Bruchids vary in weight, and therefore the 'nutritive mass' that is offered to the parasites is not constant. Their weight is greatest when the Bruchids

Figure 52. Graph **a** shows the normal fluctuations of population of two kinds of caterpillars that are injurious to cabbages, and of two groups of their enemies (black lines). Graph **b** shows how, after treatment with one type of insecticide the aphids recover more quickly than their enemies. Graph **c** shows the effect of a different insecticide that reduces the aphids more than their enemies (after Ripper, 1958).

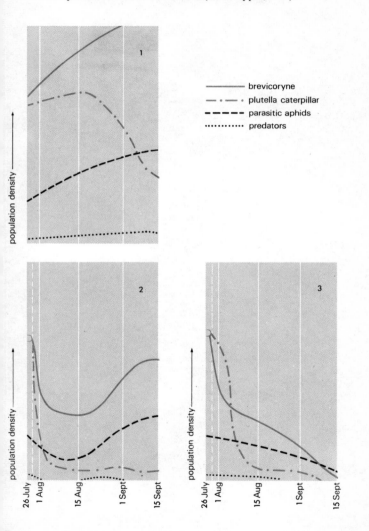

- —— brevicoryne
- —·—·— plutella caterpillar
- – – – parasitic aphids
- ·········· predators

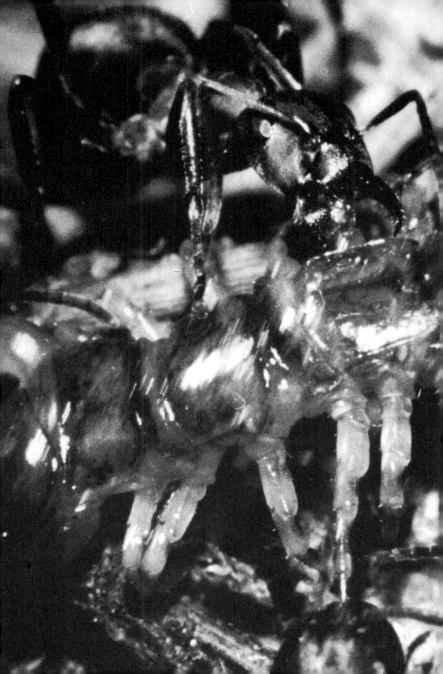

Ants attacking a centipede. The relations between predators and prey concern both the ecologist, studying the balance of animal communities, and the agriculturalist who wishes to kill pests without also destroying their natural enemies.

are by themselves, or when the degree of parasitism is low; the weight is lower when the degree of parasitism is greater. The mechanism of the variation is not very well known, except that it is irregular. In the presence of two parasites at once the progeny of the host decreases, as would be expected with more parasites, but the reduction is of the same order as with one parasite, and is not twice as great. All the same, Smith claims that multiple parasitism is more effective than a single parasite, though Utida's experiments indicate that this is not always true.

In the course of a mathematical study of parasitism that is still famous, Nicholson postulated the existence of regular fluctuations of the two populations, parasite and host, as well as the establishment of an equilibrium after a certain time. In practice, at least in the cases that we are considering at present, there are certainly fluctuations, but they are irregular and abrupt. Those which concern the parasite are on a smaller scale than those of the host, and the relative densities at the point of equilibrium hardly ever remain constant. That of the host tends to rise after a certain time, while the equilibrium density of the parasite tends to dwindle, as if its biological vitality were falling.

There are even certain paradoxical effects to be noted. For instance, if *Callosobruchus sinensis* and *C. quadrimaculatus* are reared together, *sinensis* disappears in a few generations. On the other hand the introduction of a hymenopterous parasite reduces the populations of the two Bruchids at the same time, and then they both remain in existence together. Takahashi pointed out another paradox when rearing the flour moth *Ephestia* in the presence of two different parasites (*Habrobracon* and *Cimodus*). The latter has no great effect, but on the other hand the former cuts down the population of *Ephestia* heavily, though this is able to keep itself going; now when the *Ephestia* is attacked by the two parasites together it remains in greater numbers than if it is attacked by the *Cimodus* only.

Many other examples have been described, and all the mathematical theory of relations between parasite and prey has been built up on them. But it is still, as I have said, a laboratory study.

Figure 53. The upper graph shows the normal fluctuations of
population of two mites (green line) and of their most important
enemies (black lines) during spring and summer. The lower graph
shows that application of various insecticides may reduce the
population of predaceous bugs (*Hemiptera*) and that the population of
mites may actually become greater as a result (after Redenz-Rusch, 1959).

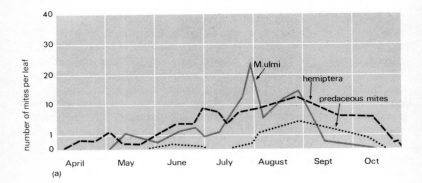

(a)

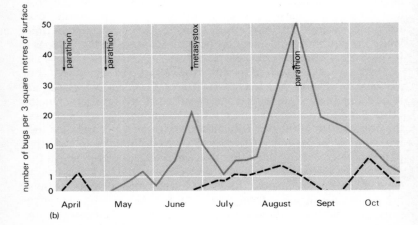

(b)

Now what is there in common between a parasite working in a confined space, on a grain-feeding insect with a very special diet, and what can be observed going on in nature? Without wishing to discourage such research – very little. I think the biologists who carry out such experiments should be urged at least to *vary* the conditions of their experiments to a greater extent. For instance, what would happen in receptacles a hundred times as big? Utida has forecast that if the dimensions of the breeding receptacle are increased for the same quantity of food, then the rate of reproduction of the Bruchids will fall, and that of the parasite will increase; without knowing why, of course.

Criticisms of mathematical ecology by field workers

As I have said earlier, not only the progressive development of a homogeneous population, but also the interaction of a parasite and its prey, have given mathematicians a tempting problem. Whole numbers of scientific journals are filled with their learned deductions, in which they imagine all the possible variations in the interaction between host and parasite. But the reality is always bigger than what can be imagined, and it must be admitted that this mathematical work can only rarely be applied to conditions in the field. Not that it is useless, I repeat, but that too many factors remain unknown for it to be possible to pass directly from mathematical ecology to field ecology.

In any case it must also be admitted that in respect of parasites and their prey the mathematicians are cheerfully and rashly wide of the mark. Thompson, for example, admitted that according to his calculations the parasite should exterminate its host completely, and thereby commit suicide. But this is to overlook the great sensitivity of parasites to climatic variations, to which they are less resistant than their hosts, as many pieces of work have shown. Only this factor will get us out of the consequences of 'cumulative parasitism'. An ecological catastrophe may lead to the extermination of the parasites if they are few in number, or to the extermination of the host if it is heavily parasitised, but calculations show that this would need a lapse of time very much longer than that forecast in Thompson's cycles. When these catastrophes follow each other at short intervals the host and its parasite are exterminated, but if the succession is less rapid, then the destruction of the host by the parasite is slowed down, but not stopped. Most of the time the interval between catastrophes is such that the host and the parasite attain a sort of 'oscillating equilibrium', which safeguards their joint existence.

Another snag about mathematical methods is their arbitrary choice of parameters and the disastrous assumptions they make. For example the principal dogmas of the 'mathematical demographers' are 1 that the population increases in a geometrical progression provided that there are no obstacles such as limited space, limited food, or any other environmental factors; 2 that the growth of population is continuous, and can be regarded as progressing by infinitesimal steps, and therefore amenable to the methods of the calculus; and 3 that it is the density of the population per unit of time that regulates its consequent development or inhibition.

Superimposed on these are a second set of assertions, this time relating to the population of the parasite, which has to suit itself to a host population governed by the three rules, 1, 2, 3.

Now, as Ullyett has said, these rules are not precise. In the first place the geometrical growth of a population is valid only if there is no kind of interruption, either seasonal or physiological. This hardly ever happens in the culture of *Tribolium* or *Drosophila*, and above all never in nature. Even in the laboratory every observer knows that animals *very often* show gross variations in their reproductive powers, when everything else is kept constant, and that up to now these have been difficult to explain. Although the *real* curve that represents the level of a population is no more than a series of peaks separated by deep troughs, and lends itself badly to the infinitesimal calculus, the mathematician gets out of it by joining together the peaks by a continuous line, by taking samples

Figure 54. A parasite may produce fewer eggs if it does not have the stimulus of the continuous presence of a possible host. Diagram 4 shows that after passing an increasing number of days without a host, the average daily egg-laying falls steadily. The other diagrams show the effect of having a suitable host present for only part of the time. Host *Acrolepia*; parasite *Diadromus* (after Labeyrie).

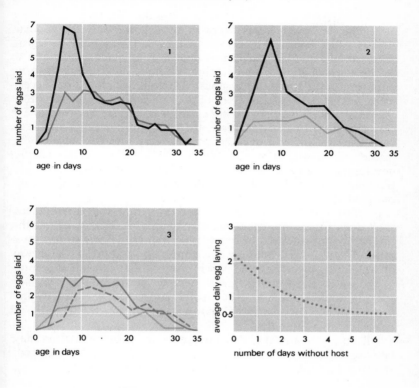

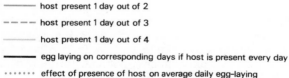

——— host present 1 day out of 2

- - - - host present 1 day out of 3

——— host present 1 day out of 4

——— egg laying on corresponding days if host is present every day

······· effect of presence of host on average daily egg-laying

at regular and equal intervals, or by considering only the population of adult insects. All these are tricks that may be quite legitimate, *so long as it is remembered that they are being employed.*

The overpopulation which brings about an automatic drop in numbers itself depends on a series of factors, which are not necessarily related to the single factor of the sufficiency of food available. We have already seen a striking example of this in the work of Le Gay Brereton. In every example, the effects of overpopulation are very complex, difficult to interpret, and vary with the stage of the insect's life-history. For example in the flies of the genus *Lucilia* developing on a cadaver, the early stages are much more vulnerable to competition, either intra- or interspecific, than are later stages; but parasitism is worst in the pupal stage.

It must not be forgotten, in addition, that the environment itself does not remain constant; it is, as the Americans say 'conditioned' by the presence of other living things. This is so not only in the *Tribolium* jar, but also in a population of *Lucilia*, the larvae of which excrete an enzyme which brings about external digestion of the meat. Even aphids greatly change the plant that they are sucking, and which may react to the substances excreted by the aphids, either by metabolic changes, or by morbid growth of tissue, as in plant-galls.

Ullyett also comments that the same density of population may be observed after completely different sets of factors have changed, showing that these cannot be considered in isolation.

Random pursuit

A condition *sine qua non* of mathematical theories of biology is that animals, such as parasites, distribute their eggs at random in a uniform manner, and in a uniform environment. In the first place there is no such thing in nature as a uniform environment. Even in a cultivated field differences of microclimate, or others arising from the nature of the soil make it impossible to equate every bit of ground to every other. Yet this postulate of uniform distribution allows theories of parasitism to be conveniently constructed, in which only the number of parasites and the number of prey need to be considered, and which apply equally to all parts of the area. Now the parasites never distribute eggs at random, in such a way that every host has an equal chance of receiving one. In the first place they very often distinguish hosts that have been already parasitised from those that have not; and furthermore, the parasites do not hunt at random, but are influenced by innumerable tropisms and conditioning factors. The hunter is subject to the hazards of the chase

Thus *Bembex* wasps hunt for preference in the pastures where they can prey on the *Lucilia* living there; Drosophilids are attracted by fermenting fruit, bees by flowers; females of *Pimpla ruficollis*, which lay their eggs in the pine noctuid moth, are attracted by the smell of pine, the louse by sources of heat between 28° and 31°C, which suggest that a suitable host is near.

As Thompson (1939) remarked, it is a matter of common sense. The parasitic insects and their hosts are both very small, and scattered within an environment that is vast in relation to their own size; their very short life leaves no time for random hunting if their senses do not guide them from the start. Laing (1938), studying *Trichogramma evanescens* shut up in a Petri dish, found that they searched at random until they found their first host egg, but then their searching behaviour altered and became much more orderly. One might even ask whether the initial random searching might not be an effect of imprisonment in the Petri dish.

In the same way Ullyett noticed that during releases of the parasite *Chelonus* against *Loxostega*, the hymenopteron swooped down for preference on bushes of *Pentzia* on which the caterpillar lived. Now these bushes are hardly higher than the beetroot on which live other species of *Loxostega* that are the original hosts of the *Chelonus*, which is thus adapted to hunt at a certain height above ground. In contrast *Meteorus*, another parasite of *Loxostega*, is interested only in the dense masses of silk with which the caterpillars cover the vegetation, and shows no concern for their height.

Parasite, host and environment

There are odd cases in which the parasite, the host and the environment influence each other in unforeseen ways. Such is the case of a small caterpillar, *Plutella maculipennis*, which is attacked by different parasites when it is living on cabbage and when it is living on water-cress. Here a known factor, the environment, alters not only the intensity of attack of the parasite, but its very nature. Everything is altered; a formula that expresses the mortality of the *Plutella* as a function of the number of its parasites when on cabbage will be valueless when it is on water-cress. In addition the Staphylinidae that attack *Plutella* on cabbage vary in number according to the state of cultivation of the field; when the soil is right the population of these predators falls and that of *Plutella* grows, at least if the cabbage aphids are not scarce at the time. In fact the *Plutella* harbours different parasites, which also feed on aphids, and which attack the *Plutella* only when there are not enough aphids (Ullyett). All this, it will be agreed, adds up to a pattern of interacting factors of terrible complexity. I have not set this out just to bait the mathematicians, but this is how things really happen in nature.

This is nothing compared with the behaviour of *Diadromus*, an ichneumonid parasite of pupae of *Acrolepia*, which has been studied by Labeyrie (1963). In this instance the fecundity of the parasite is dependent upon whether or not it meets its hosts with a certain frequency. If the host insect is less frequent than this, then the eggs of the ichneumon are reabsorbed in the oviducts. The presence of its host, and the act of piercing, stimulate the *Diadromus* even though it may be offered only empty cocoons of *Acrolepia*. It pushes its ovipositor into these, and though it may lay no eggs, this act is sufficient to retain the fecundity of those that are waiting to be laid. These impressive observations raise a suspicion that other parasites may be in the same situation as *Diadromus*, and this should be enough to sow a seed of doubt in the minds of the mathematicians.

The success of biological control

All these possibilities of error should not lead us to forget once again the spectacular successes of biological control. Even if these are few in number, and even if they rest on a fortunate combination of circumstances, they nevertheless point a way that is full of promise. To follow this trail needs much more advanced biological knowledge. This is a time to recall what Peckett and Patterson (1953) said: 'The empirical methods that the economic entomologists are forced to use are often of doubtful value, and should be looked upon as temporary measures, to be constantly re-examined'.

Insects against insects: commercial use of ladybirds

The most striking of the historical examples of the use of insects against other insects is the commercial use of ladybirds. These were known to be fierce predators of aphids and of scale-insects, but how to get enough of them? The first idea was to make use of one of their oddest peculiarities, that of hibernating in vast numbers, always in the same places, under the same stones, generally on hills or mountains. Sometimes enough could be found to fill a bowl. It must be remembered that it is not the same individuals that are found each year, since the life-cycle of adult ladybirds is much too short for that. It must therefore be assumed that there is some way in which the ladybirds are attracted from many kilometres radius.

Examples are known of chemical attractants that would have this effect, for example those by which the females of certain large nocturnal moths, the Sphingids, attract their males. Mell showed that the males could find their females over a distance of eleven kilometres! Now two things about this business are certain. One is that the attractive substance is emitted by quite a small gland in the abdomen of the female; this gland can be dissected out, and will cause a male to try to copulate with it, even though it is almost too small to be seen with the naked eye. Secondly, on the most favourable estimate, the dilution of this substance at a radius of eleven kilometres can hardly be greater than one molecule per cubic metre. Obviously this poses a lot of problems. How does a substance 'smell' at such a dilution? And again, how can it have a directive effect, and lead the males to its source? But we haven't time to go into that.

Growers on the coastal plains of California complained of the plant-bugs that devastated their orchards, and that is where Carnes in 1910 had the idea of collecting a mass of ladybirds (*Hippodamia*). Here I will hand over the story to Balachowsky, whose excellent treatise (1951) contains a host of similar examples.

After 1910 Carnes conceived the idea of transporting hibernating ladybirds from the mountains down into the fruit-farms on the coastal plain to attack the plant-bugs there. In the event this idea had a great success, in spite of the heavy loss of 50–75% of the ladybirds in transit. The use of insecticides gradually displaced this technique, although between the years 1924–36 in the State of Washington a society sold ladybirds at 6–8 dollars per litre, each litre containing from 8,000–10,000 individual insects. In 1943, during the Second World War, as a result of the shortage of nicotine and other contact insecticides, Carnes's technique was revived on a large scale by C. W. Hippers of the Yuba Co of California, who put *Hippodamia* into canvas bags of two gallons (nine litres) capacity, and induced an artificial hibernation by keeping them at 4–6°C. This society distributed colonies of ladybirds in this way among the farmers of different parts of America at a rate of two dollars and a half per gallon. A mortality of less than 10% was guaranteed. Certain growers bought up to 3–5 gallons of ladybirds, more than 50,000 insects, for a single orchard. Hatch and Tanasse reported that in the course of the year 1936, 1,160 gallons (nearly five tons!) of ladybirds were distributed in this way in the fruit-growing valley of Yatima, in Washington State.

All this took place before the modern period in biological control, and it was still a matter, if one may say so, of rule of thumb methods. But the immense orchards of California made it possible to finance and test all kinds of different methods of control, even expensive and risky ones, because so much was at stake. This is what happened at the time of the dramatic invasion of citrus plantations in California by scale-insects of the genus *Pseudococcus*. They had no local enemy that was powerful enough to deal with them, so the entomologists thought of an Australian ladybird *Cryptolaemus montrouzieri*, which had been known since 1890 as a bitter enemy of several species of *Pseudococcus*. Unfortunately this ladybird passes the winter as a pupa in dead leaves, and under bark, and suffers a heavy mortality which may be as high as 98%. It was not enough, therefore, just to introduce this control, it had to be built up. For this purpose there were erected, first at Riverside, California, and later in Spain, ladybird factories. In enormous constant-temperature chambers the ladybirds developed *en masse* during the winter on potato-shoots infested with *Pseudococcus*. Attempts have even been made, with some success, to keep Aphids and Coccids in deep-freeze, so that they could be offered to the ladybirds at any time without having to rear them on potato; but this was not profitable enough.

According to Balachowsky, in 1928 the giant insectaria of Riverside distributed 48 million ladybirds into the orange groves of California. The excellent results did not prevent entomologists from looking for still better methods, that is for a parasite that would reproduce by itself, without having to be cultivated. In 1927 Compere found in Australia, in the original locality from which came the scale-insects that were so devastating in California, two chalcids (Hymenoptera) which would attack the scale-insect. The one that was introduced into California reproduced so well that it virtually ended the problem of *Pseudococcus* in California, and greatly lessened the importance of the ladybird factories.

This recalls the celebrated, but earlier example of *Icerya purchasi*, the fluted scale or cottony cushion scale, a giant species from Australia. It appeared suddenly in citrus orchards in California, and also in those of the south of France. The introduction of a ladybird *Rodalia cardinalis*, also of Australian origin, enabled the scourge to be choked off with a 'phenomenal efficiency'. There was no need to set up *Rodalia* factories, since it built up its own populations very well by its own efforts. These tiny insects are among the most valuable allies of man, and it is easy to understand why in France they are called '*bêtes à bon Dieu*', and the superstitious believe that it is unlucky to kill them.

This has been a very brief account of the complete success that followed the introduction of an Australian parasite into the very different climate and biological environment of California. Naturally, there have been problems, and many unsuccessful attempts, but in the first part of this chapter I stressed the unknowns that beset every problem in biological control, and I do not need to labour this point again. All the same it must be pointed out that the state of mind of the early specialists in this field was, and still is, very different from that of the bio-mathematicians. The pioneers did not bother about the theoretical problem, which they did not have the means to solve. They simply tried out an experiment which succeeded. In the existing state of knowledge this is to give proof of wisdom.

There are all the same a certain number of practical considerations familiar to entomologists, which it may not be without value to recall at this point, after Balachowsky (1951). In the first place the acclimatisation of a pest in a country far removed from its place of origin, bears no relation to the possibilities of acclimatising one of its parasites. The rarity of the parasite in its original locality, and the fact that it seems to be unimportant there, are equally irrelevant to the chances of acclimatising it in the invasion area, and to the chance that it may turn out to be important there. Balachowsky rightly quotes the recent example of a pine sawfly *Gilpinia hercyniae*, which is very harmful in Canada. A great many of its parasites have been tried as possible controls, but only one of them has succeeded. This is a Tachinid fly from Bohemia, *Prosturmia bohemica*, which is *extremely rare* in its homeland.

Finally Balachowsky states that: 'It may happen that a series of parasites, each of which has a poor effect by itself, can act in concert and produce a "resultant parasitism" that may have a stabilising effect on the outbreak of a pest'.

The testing of insecticides may require a long series of individual experiments, using different chemicals, and the same chemicals in a range of concentrations. Sometimes this requires several kilograms of flies per day, so that rearing on a massive scale is called for.

Modern spraying equipment makes the application of insecticides and herbicides a quick and thorough operation.

Can insects be infected with disease?

When biological control is being discussed one of the ideas that comes naturally to mind is to infect harmful insects with bacteria, fungus or virus diseases. On this subject there are some ancient tentative experiments, which were carried out at a time when little was known about the pathology of insects: for example the idea of combating 'white grubs' (chafer larvae) with the help of a fungus which 'mummifies' them, and to use other fungi against locust swarms or house-flies.

These researches took place in particular just after the First World War, and were poorly planned, or carried out with inadequate resources. Then, little by little, at the time of the Second World War and after there grew up a genuine science of insect pathology of which Steinhaus in America was soon one of the high priests. This was an immense and mysterious field of study, which had been pioneered earlier by such men as Paillot, one of the most distinguished minds that we have had in France. Unfortunately he came too soon, and was too much on his own.

Let us begin by raising an objection that will come to mind immediately, that the diseases of insects are not at all the same as those of man, and *vice versa*. Bacteria that are terribly virulent for man may have no effect on insects. It is only a dozen years since it was being told how the intolerable Argentine Ant had established several colonies in Paris, notably in the Institut Pasteur. So much so that the alarmed staff of the Institut Pasteur were telling dark stories about ants that had penetrated the seal of a container and were living in the midst of a culture of a terrible virus, apparently without ill effect. I do not know whether this anecdote was true or not, except to the extent that it demonstrated that we may be wasting our time if we try to infect ants with our own diseases.

This fundamental difference between man and ants makes it possible to cultivate safely strains of disease organisms that are lethal to insects, and indeed to select them for greater virulence.

The first progress in studying the pathology of insects came, as might have been expected, from that readily available insect, the honey-bee. This insect, which has aroused men's interest from time immemorial suffers from a variety of illnesses which may affect either the larvae or the adults, and there is a big literature on this subject, which we cannot go into here. All the same I should like to mention two matters, that are odd from quite different angles.

There is a disease called American foul brood, caused by *Bacillus larvae*, which makes the larvae rot in their cells. Now if a sample is taken of the disgusting broth that is produced no other germ can be cultured from it except *Bacillus larvae*; from which it follows that this bacillus is able to secrete an antibiotic powerful enough to destroy every other form of bacterial life in a mass of material in full tide of decomposition. Not only is this deduction accepted as true, but the antibiotic has even been extracted and it was most interesting. All the same the researches have not been pursued. . . .

For another thing the Swiss biologist Fyg has started another hare by being one of the first to study *diseases of queen bees* which are quite different from those of workers. It was not long before he had found a dozen of these, each one of which deserved a detailed study. I consider these studies most important, not only in so far as they concern bees, but also for their import in the general war against ants and termites, insects which produce terrible outbreaks, and which are most difficult to combat by accepted methods such as insecticides. On the other hand the least that can be said is that the pathology of ants and termites is still in its infancy; I do not know if a score of works on this subject could be listed. Perhaps one could develop the study of diseases, not of the workers, but of the winged sexual forms of ants and termites, which can be obtained in large numbers quite easily at certain seasons of the year. Who knows whether, by taking inspiration from the work of Fyg we could not find diseases that could be turned to practical use.

In general insects seem more vulnerable to diseases caused by fungi than to bacterial diseases, no doubt as a result of the special properties of the insect integument. Moreover, death from a fungus attack is most spectacular to see, and perhaps that is why it was first to be studied. There is the historic example of the 'white grubs' (chafer larvae) which are attacked and 'mummified' by the fungus *Beauveria*. This has been known since 1809, but the disease was detected for the first time in France in the Orne by the entomologist Le Moult. He sent his 'mummies' to the well-known biologist Giard, who made a celebrated study of the disease and of the fungus.

Later, an attempt was made to apply this commercially, but in spite of the premature enthusiasm aroused by the first results, it soon became clear that epidemics of *Beauveria* follow laws that we do not understand. No results came from burying the spores of the fungus in the soil. The natural mortality of the grubs was never exceeded, in spite of excellent results in laboratory tests. It is true that in science nothing is ever finished, and certain very recent results by Polish workers have done a little to raise *Beauveria* out of the discredit into which it has fallen as an agent in biological control.

Entomologists have had better luck with *bacillary* diseases, which have finally been successfully cultivated and disseminated. For instance the Americans found in them a way of dealing with the terrible Japanese chafer *Popillia japonica*, which was formerly a great problem because of its fabulous powers of reproduction. 'Since 1944', says Balachowsky 'the research centre at Moorestown in the USA has distributed spores for use against the larvae of *Popillia*. Larvae infected from a virulent culture are incubated in batches of 500 in terrarium at 30°C for 10–12 days. After this interval the infected larvae are sifted out . . . and placed in a refrigerator at 0–2°C to immobilise them, and then they are kept in ice until enough individuals have been accumulated. To make a powder of spores, the larvae are crushed in special mincers, and the particles thus obtained are suspended in water. A supporting medium of calcium carbonate is added, and then evaporated slowly in order to obtain about one thousand million spores per gram of dried substance. This dried compound is then mixed with a neutral diluent such as talc to bring it down to one hundred million spores per gram, and the powder is then ready for use, and is stored.

A rotary drill applies this powder to maize at the rate of two grams per seed-hole, at intervals of ten feet in every direction, and then it is estimated that the entire area of soil is invaded by spores of *B. popilliae* within three years. In areas infested with *Popillia japonica* where forty-four larvae per square foot could be counted in 1940 there are today no more than five per square foot.

Happily France has not lagged behind in this work. Grison, Maury and Vago have carried on large scale experiments since

1958 on the slopes of Mount Ventoux, where processionary cater-pillars devastated the pine-woods. For this purpose they have used not a bacterium, but one of those strange viruses of insects which produce in the cells mysterious polyhedric clusters of crystals. Hence the name 'polyhedric disease', or 'polyhedrosis'. Five hundred hectares of pines have thus received in 1958 and 1959 a powdering at a concentration of twenty million polyhedric clusters per gram. The long-term effects must be studied for many years to come. As for the immediate effects, these are spectacular; in the course of an inspection in 1961, observers were able to find only eighteen egg-masses of the processionary moth in twenty-two hectares.

Yet the bacillus that is most widely used at the present time and which is also being studied in France is *Bacillus thuringiensis*, the culture of which is completely industrialised. There are now veritable little factories with the sole purpose of manufacturing it, and it seems able to start fatal epidemics among a great many harmful caterpillars. It should be possible to make use of it on a very big scale, and this will be welcomed by bee-keepers, because this bacillus appears to be quite harmless to bees.

Before leaving the subject of induced epidemics we must mention an original and effective method of getting rid of mosquitoes; that is, to give them worms. In fact, many Nematode worms are known to be parasites of insects, which put up with their unwanted guest more or less successfully, but it is only recently that the idea has occurred of using them in biological control. Certain species are being cultured, and larvae of the wax-moth (*Galleria*) infested with them. All that is needed is to scatter into the ponds and lakes dead caterpillars of the moth, riddled with young forms of the nematodes, which then migrate to mosquito larvae. It should be said right away that the worms do not kill the mosquito larvae by their mere presence, but as a final touch of refinement, these nematodes are vectors of a bacterium that is lethal to the mosqui-toes. So effective is this that 60–70% of the mosquitoes disappear from ponds so treated.

So-called 'psychic' methods

The idea of using their own behaviour as a weapon against insects is no longer new. The oldest of such devices is the *light trap*. One only needs to see the mass of insects that comes to burn itself at a flame to realise the origin of that idea. I do not know how many light traps have been invented with this idea in mind, including the most varied and often the most whimsical, fitted sometimes with suction apparatus the better to catch the insects, giving out light of all possible wavelengths, including ultra-violet. Certainly the number of captures is impressive, but the final results are rather meagre from the point of view of applied entomology.

There are many reasons for this. In the first place the light never attracts one hundred per cent of the individuals of a species, in nature, even though it gives good results in the laboratory. Certain calculations suggest that fewer than 1 % of the population comes to the light trap. For another thing it is often only the males that are attracted, though obviously the capture of egg-laying females would be more profitable. And finally, careful experiments, carried out over a long period by ecologists of the English school, demonstrate that insects, and especially moths, in flight do not keep to one level; all stages are found from one metre above the ground to a height of sixteen metres, and the species that are caught by traps set at different levels are never the same.

Indeed one sex may habitually fly five or six metres higher than the other; and again the level of flight may vary with the season, or the weather, or the different meteorological conditions at different times of night. In short, failing some new discovery, which is always possible, light traps at present seem useless in applied entomology.

What about chemical attractants or repellents, whether natural or synthetic? The effect of these on insects has been known for a long time, and here, luckily, the results are more encouraging. First, remember a very surprising fact, that many harmful insects attack only a small number of species of plants, within the same family. These insects are said to be 'monophagous', or 'oligopha-gous'. Now in most instances we know that this choice is dictated by chemical factors, though we do not know what these factors are. Yet another example of the empirical state of our knowledge! And this is true even for pests that are very well known; for instance it is only a short time since it was discovered what chemical attracted *Doryphora* to potatoes. However, once this factor is known, imagine the enthusiasm of the geneticist, who will be able to estimate the content of this attractant that is in different species of Solanaceae, and then to try to develop and select strains in which the attractant is at a minimum . . . etc.

Attractants have had a practical application that is more directly interesting in the battle against the Gypsy Moth *Porthetria dispar* in America. At first the operators were content to use clumsy methods, macerating in spirit the abdomens of old female moths that had been obtained in great numbers by rearing. Later, at the right season, these were placed on tree trunks, and would then attract male moths from as far as four kilometres. This provided a method of investigation that was very effective, and which was capable of revealing the presence of the pest in areas where it had not been suspected to be. The power and the specific nature of the chemical attraction raised other hopes. It is not unreasonable to hope that by this means so many males might be destroyed that most of the females would remain unfertilised. Moreover very recently the patience of certain American biologists and chemists has been rewarded; for ten years, they have laboured to extract and to analyse the sexual attractant of female *Porthetria*, and now they have done so. Now if large quantities of a powerful chemical attrac-tant can be obtained without having to rear thousands of female moths all the hopes of a practical application will be realised.

Methods of self-slaughter

Although this is not strictly an example of 'psychic' control, another technique must be mentioned here which is equally

directed against male insects. Once again this has been developed
in the U.S.A., and once again by veritable 'insect factories'. This
time it is the battle undertaken in Texas against the terrible screw-
worm of cattle, larvae of the fly *Callitroga*. The idea was to
sterilise male flies by radioactivity, and then release them, thus
*swamping the fertile males of the natural population in an ocean of
sterile males.* Since the female flies mate only once it ought to be
possible in this way to reduce considerably the chances that a female
has of meeting a fertile male, while simultaneously increasing the
percentage of infertile matings. This seems quite feasible, but not
without considerable financial resources; these are easily found in
Texas where, as we know, they do not believe in half-measures.
For several years now 'breeding factories' dispersed throughout the
area where *Callitroga* is rampant have released waves of sterilised
males. The practical result – complete disappearance of the
scourge.

This is an entirely new method, which opens new horizons.
More recently the idea is to use chemical sterilants, which will
continue in operation, and if at the same time the males could be
attracted into the area where the sterilant was being distributed,
all the chances of success would be augmented. Who knows if even
the old light traps may not come into use again for this purpose?

Repellents

Repellents have many more practical applications, than attractants, especially against mosquitoes. It is thanks to these repellents that the American army was able to maintain itself in the
Burmese jungle, where mosquitoes make life intolerable to an
unprotected man. A variety of formulae have been tried, based
on synthetic substances such as dimethylphthalate.

Tests of the effectiveness of repellents are quite unpleasant.
The only really effective tests consist of 'detailing volunteers', who
smear the substance to be tested on their arms, and then put them
into a cage of mosquitoes. Then the bites are counted! It requires

To extract a few insects from a crowded rearing-jar it is convenient to make use of the insect's own behaviour. Most insects move towards the light and so if the sample tube is correctly pointed the insects will walk into it.

endless hours of this sort of testing to arrive at a composition that can be borne for several hours without irritating the skin. All the same it does not take long to find out that soaking one's garments in a bath containing certain compounds of urea is effective against mites.

Outside the field of human parasitology there are a number of applications of repellents against such things as wood-borers, including termites, and in this context excellent results have been obtained.

There remains the immense subject of the defence of green plants against their parasites. Is this possible on a large scale? No one can say, because few attempts have been made. Entomologists as a body are sceptical, and it would be necessary to find chemicals that would give a really spectacular result before they would be convinced.

I have several times had occasion to try this myself, without much success. The first attempt was against the Desert Locust, *Schistocerca gregaria*, about which I wrote my thesis a very long time ago. Along with one of my friends, Charles Menzer, I tried out a whole series of synthetic products, which had the effect of repelling locusts from the fresh legumes that we were offering to them. But tests carried out in Morocco during a locust outbreak were misleading because the substances were not soluble enough to cover the plants with a continuous film of repellent. Later Menzer prepared soluble derivatives, which we sent out for trial in Morocco; the authorities said they were not interested, because the product remained stable for only four days. All the same, some insecticides are no more stable than this, and when the locusts descend on an orchard they devastate it in a very few minutes! Ah well, as they say, there is none so deaf as he who will not hear.

Nevertheless, the use of repellents ought to be possible, even against insects as voracious as locusts. I do not need more proof of this than the experiments made in Argentina with 'Amargo' maize. This is a species of maize of which the leaves, if one knows Spanish, ought to have a bitter taste. Grasshoppers will not eat them, though they soon make a mouthful of ordinary maize. Moreover, not all substances that taste bitter to us are repellent to grasshoppers; on the other hand all substances that repel grasshoppers also taste bitter to us. For instance, the leaves of *Melia azedarach* which grasshoppers will eat only exceptionally, contain a substance that is horribly bitter, solutions of which will protect ordinary plants for a certain time. Yet the bark of this shrub is not bitter, and extracts from it are not repellent.

My last experiment with repellents, equally disappointing, concerned bees, which were annually decimated by the use of insecticides on colza, because the chemicals applied against the enemies of colza were also toxic to bees. Many laboratories, particularly those under my direction, were searching at that time for a repellent which would drive away the bees from the flowers during the dangerous period. In these laboratory tests we made use of sugar syrup, which gave very encouraging results, and it seemed very easy to keep the bees away from the syrup. But alas we had to retract after the first experiments under natural conditions. Nothing seemed capable of keeping the bees away from the flowers. Even the phenol, used in such a concentration that the flowers were burned by it, and we were inconvenienced by the smell, did not discourage the foraging bees. Things remain thus for the present, demonstrating once again the danger of applying laboratory findings too readily to natural conditions. Fortunately we have found other ways of protecting the colza without killing the bees.

Conclusion

The whole of this book, apart from a few pages, has been devoted to the populace of insects, and to means of evaluating this in order the better to fight against it. Is this the only possible viewpoint? Is the insect inevitably our enemy; can we not make use of it?

It seems that we can, and that we have not done so earlier, and more effectively, because we are slaves to preconceived ideas. Let us leave on one side the bee, which is a very special case, one of the most important of all insects not only for its honey, which man can easily dispense with, but also for its action in pollinating many plants.

The case of the red ant is less well known. It is little known that this insect is by way of becoming 'domesticated', a protector of forests, by reason of its voracious appetite, which requires almost a kilogram of insect meat per nest per day. Could we not train it to a particular prey, in the same way that von Frisch has trained bees to feed from this or that flower? Can we not conceive of mobile formicaria, which can be taken to their place of work as is done with bees needed to pollinate a field? Of course the ants have the drawback of taking with them everywhere their inseparable aphids, which are liable to infest the plants that are to be 'deparasitised'. But aphids can be attacked with the so-called 'systemic' insecticides, which lie inside the plant tissue, and will not harm the ants, though they will prevent the aphids from becoming established on the plants. The ants, deprived of the honey-dew of the aphids, could be given sugar. This is successfully done to bees, which have to be artificially fed when they are placed in an orchard to pollinate it, in numbers far in excess of the number of bees that it will support.

Outside the social insects there is another possible use of insects that has turned out to be most interesting. This is to use them against invasions of harmful plants. Balachowsky gives several striking examples of this. Certain fig-trees from Barbary (*Opuntia*, the Prickly Pear) introduced into Australia where they have no enemies, promptly invaded 25 million hectares of New South Wales, and continued to spread at the rate of half a million hectares per year. Happily Hamlin and Dodd quickly imported a small moth (*Cactoblastis*) and scale-insects of the genus *Dactylopius*, which took their toll of the disastrous fig-trees from Barbary. Before the introduction of these providential insects all other methods of elimination had failed.

The unfortunate Australian continent had no luck in another direction when Millepertuis (St John's wort, *Hypericum* sp.) proliferated in the same way, and grew to a height of one and a half metres! In 1930 it invaded 200,000 hectares of the State of Victoria, making them useless for agricultural purposes. It needed the intervention of several well-chosen Chrysomelid beetles to rid Australia effectively of it.

Balachowsky gives a dozen other examples, all equally striking, which make me ponder. How many weeds are there in Europe of which the fields ought to be rid? Herbicides introduce into the fields by the ton a whole series of molecules about which we do not know very much, and which contaminate the soil and the streams. Is this the only solution? And again, could not hoeing in orchards be replaced by some more intelligent method. Are there no insects that could be cultivated and selected to use against our own weeds? Against brambles, for example, we know already that certain *Carabus* could be used, but it is inconvenient that they also attack roses. Could not this drawback be surmounted? How many other examples could be given?

The populace of insects is only the enemy of man because he does not behave intelligently and make use of it.

Bibliography

The papers listed below are chosen for their general application, and as a guide to further reading. The many authorities listed in the text should be traced by reference to the *Zoological Record*, the *Review of Applied Entomology*, the *Journal of Economic Entomology*, and *Biological Abstracts*.

L. Adams, 1951. 'Confidence limits for the Petersen or Lincoln index used in animal population studies.' *J. Wildlife Man.* **15**: 13–19.

F. S. Andersen, 1956. 'Effects of crowding in *Endrosis sarcitrella*.' *Oikos* **7**: 215–27.

P. Ardö, 1957. 'Studies in the marine shore dune ecosystem, with special reference to the dipterous fauna.' *Opusc. ent. Lund. suppl.* **14**: 1–255.

H. Aulitzky, 1953. 'Forst meteorologische Untersuchungen an der Wald und Baumgrenzen in der Zentralalpen.' *Arch. Meteor. Georgr. Bioklim.* **4**: 294–310.

N. T. J. Bailey, 1951. 'On estimating the size of mobile populations from recapture data.' *Biometrika* **38**: 293–306.

K. S. Baweja, 1939. 'Studies on the soil fauna, with special reference to the recolonisation of the sterilised soil.' *J. anim. Ecol.* **8**: 120–61.

B. P. Beirne, 1962. 'Trends in applied biological control of insects.' *Ann. Rev. Ent.* **7**: 387–400.

G. Y. Bey-Bienko, 1961. 'On some regularities in the changes of the invertebrate fauna during the utilisation of virgin steppe' [in Russian with English summary; extracts in *Uvarov*, 1964]. *Rev. Ent. U.R.S.S.* **40**: 763–75.

W. O. Billings and R. I. Morris, 1951. 'Reflection of visible and infra-red radiation from leaves of different ecological groups.' *Amer. J. Bot.* **38**: 327–31.

L. C. Birch, 1953. 'Experimental background to the studies of the distribution and abundance of insects. *III*. The relation between innate capacity for increase and survival of different species of beetles living together on the same food.' *Evolution* **7**: 136–44.

L. C. Birch, T. Park and M. B. Frank, 1951. 'The effect of intraspecies competition on the fecundity of two species of flour beetle.' *Evolution* **5**: 116–32.

F. S. Bodenheimer and M. Schiffer, 1952. 'Mathematical studies in animal populations.' *Acta Biotheoretica* **10**: 23–56.

M. Boness, 1953. 'Die Fauna der Wiesen und besonderer Berücksichtung der Mahd (ein Beitrag zur Agrarökologie). *Z. Morph. Oekol. Tiere*, Berlin **42**: 225–77.

244

R. van den Bosch and V. M. Stern, 1962. 'The integration of chemical and biological control of arthropod pests.' *Ann. Rev. Ent.* **7**: 366–86.

J. Bowden, 1954. 'The stem-borer problem in tropical cereal crops.' *Rep. 6th Commonwealth Ent. Conf., London*: 104–7.

L. Broadbent, 1950. 'The microclimate of the potato-crop.' *Quart. J. R. Meteor. Soc.* **76**: 330.

T. Burnett, 1953. 'Effects of temperature and parasite density on the rate of increase of an insect parasite.' *Ecology* **34**: 322–8.

R. Carpenter, 1936. 'Quantitative community studies of land animals.' *J. anim. Ecol.* **5**: 231–45.

C. Caussanel, 1965. 'Recherches préliminaires sur le peuplement de Coléoptères d'une plage sableuse atlantique.' *Ann. Soc. ent. France.* **NS 1**: 197–248.

R. Cayrol, 1956. 'Influence de l'alimentation et de l'effet de groupe sur la pigmentation des chenilles de *Plusia gamma*.' *C.R. Acad. Sc.* **243**: 601–2.

R. Chauvin, 1948. 'De la méthode en écologie entomologique.' *Rev. Scient.* **86**: 627–33.

R. Chauvin, 1950. 'Méthodes de mesures physiques et méthodes de prélèvement en écologie entomologique.' *Colloq. int. Ecol. C.N.R.S.*: 313–23.

R. Chauvin, 1952. 'L'effet de groupe.' *Symposium international sur les insectes sociaux. C.N.R.S.*: 81–90.

R. Chauvin, 1956. *Physiologie de l'insecte. Le comportement, les grandes fonctions, écophysiologie.* Paris: Inst. Nat. Rech. Agronomique. 918 pp. 104 figs.

R. Chauvin, 1956. 'Quelques phénomènes étranges en rapport avec la météorologie, et qui intéressent les biologistes.' *Année biol.* Paris **32**: 233–45.

R. Chauvin, 1956. 'Biologie de l'insecte: réflexions sur l'écologie entomologique.' *Rev. Zool. Agric. Bordeaux.* **I** 55: 38–57; **II** 55: 86; 100; **III** 56: 19–27; **IV** 56: 55–71.

R. Chauvin, 1956. *Vie et mœurs des insectes.* Paris. 250 pp.

H. C. Chiang and A. C. Hodson, 1950. 'An analytical study of population growth in *Drosophila melanogaster*.' *Ecol. Monogr.* **20**: 173–206.

O. R. Clarck, 'Interception of rainfall by prairie grasses, weeds and certain crop plants.' *Ecol. Monogr.* **10**: 243–77.

G. Clément, 1956. 'Observations sur l'essaimage d'*Anacanthotermes ochraceus* Burm. (Isoptera).' *Bull. Soc. ent. France.* **61**: 98–103.

L. C. Cole, 1946. 'Theory for analysing contagiously distributed populations.' *Ecology* **27**: 327–41.

A. C. Crombie, 1942. 'The effects of crowding upon the oviposition of grain infesting insects.' *J. exp. Biol.* **9**: 311–41.

M. J. Delany, 1953. 'Studies on the microclimate of *Calluna* heathland.' *J. anim. Ecol.* **22**: 227–39.

M. Diem, 1954. 'Das Mikroklima in einen kunstlich beregneten Tabakbestand.' *Arch. Met. Geoph. Bioklim.* **5**: 216–33.

W. W. Dowdy, 1951. 'Further ecological studies on stratification of arthropods.' *Ecology* **32**: 37–52.

G. and S. Elkholm, 1956. 'On a mass occurrence of insects on a shore at Pellinge.' *Notul. ent.*, Helsinki **36**: 8–11.

P. E. Ellis, 1951. 'The marching behaviour of hoppers of the African migratory locust *Locusta migratoria migratorioides* in the laboratory.' *Antilocust Bulletin No. 7.* 46 pp.

F. A. Fenton and D. E. Howell, 1957. 'A comparison of five methods of sampling alfalfa fields for arthropod populations.' *Ann. ent. Soc. America* **50**: 606–11.

R. A. Fisher, A. S. Corbet and C. B. Williams, 1943. 'The relation between the number of species and the number of individuals in a random sample of an animal population.' *J. anim. Ecol.* **12**: 45–58.

R. Geiger, 1950. *The climate near the ground.* Harvard Univ. Press. 481 pp.

G. Guyer and R. Hutson, 1955. 'A comparison of sampling techniques utilised in an ecological study of aquatic insects.' *J. econ. Ent.* **48**: 662–5.

H. Gisin, 1949. 'L'écologie.' *Acta Biotheoretica* **A9**: 89–100.

J. P. Glasgow, 1963. *The distribution and abundance of tsetse.* London, 241 pp.

T. W. Goodwin, 1953. 'The pigments in colour phases of the larvae of *Plusia gamma*.' *Biochem. J.* **55**: 834–8.

T. G. Grigor'eva, 1960. 'On the method of protecting cereal cultures in the zone of development of virgin and long-fallow land cultivation' [in Russian; extracts from *Uvarov*, 1964]. *Rev. Ent. U.R.S.S.* **39**: 509–20.

I. M. Hall and V. M. Stern, 1962. 'Comparison of *Bacillus thuringiensis* and chemical insecticides for control of the alfalfa caterpillar.' *J. econ. Ent.* **55(6)**: 862–5.

I. C. Hamlin and others, 1949. 'Field studies of the alfalfa weevil and its environment.' *U.S. Dept. Agr. Tech. Bull.* **975.** 84 pp.

A. C. Hardy and R. S. Milnes, 1938. 'Studies in the distribution of insects by aerial currents.' *J. anim. Ecol.* **7**: 198–229.

J. E. Harker, 1956. 'Factors controlling the diurnal rhythm of activity of *Periplaneta americana* L.' *J. exp. Biol.* **33**: 224–34.

C. Henneberger, 1950. 'Tagesgang und Komponenten der Abkühlungs-

246

grosse.' *Arch. Meteor. Geoph. Bioklim.* **B2:** 86–119.

B. Huber, 1952. 'Der Einfluss der Vegetation auf die Schwankungen des CO_2 gehaltes der Atmosphäre.' *Arch. Meteor. Geoph. Bioklim.* **4:** 154–67.

B. Hurpin, 1956. 'Influence des conditions atmosphériques sur les sorties préalimentaires du hanneton commun (*Melolontha melolontha* L.) *Ann. Epiphyt.*' Paris (**C**)**7:** 333–61.

G. G. Jackson, 1939. 'The analysis of an animal population.' *J. anim. Ecol.* **8:** 238–46.

G. G. Jackson, 1950. 'The comparison of suction trap, sticky trap and townet for the quantitative sampling of small airborne insects.' *Ann. appl. Biol.* **37:** 268–85.

G. G. Jackson and L. R. Taylor, 1955. 'The measurement of insect density in the air.' **I.II** Laboratory practice 4: 187–92; 235–9.

G. G. Jackson and L. R. Taylor, 1955. 'The development of large suction traps for airborne insects.' *Ann. appl. Biol.* **43:** 51–61.

C. G. Johnson, 1952. 'The changing numbers of *Aphis fabae* flying at crop level in relation to the current weather and to the population of the crop.' *Ann. appl. Biol.* **39:** 525–47.

M. Kato, 1953. 'Microclimate of the flowers of *Chrysanthemum leucanthemum* and the behaviour of a dermestid beetle *Anthrenus verbasci.*' *Seitaigaku Kenkyu* **9:** 179–86.

K. H. L. Key, 1950. 'A critique of the phase theory of locusts.' *Quart. Rev. Biol.* **25:** 363–407.

W. Kruel, 1957. 'Bemerkeinswerte Auftreten von Waldinsekten unter dem Einfluss klimatisch-meteorologisch Faktoren der letzen 10 Jahre im östlichen Deutschland.' *Z. angew Ent.* **41:** 386–94.

G. de Lattin, 1957. 'Die Ausbreitungszentren der holarktischen Landtierwelt.' *Verh. dtsch. zool. Ges.* **1956:** 380–410.

J. Lepointe, 1956. 'Méthodes de captures dans l'écologie des arbres.' *Vie et Milieu* **7:** 233–41.

P. H. Leslie and T. Park, 1949. 'The intrinsic rate of natural increase of *Tribolium castaneum* Herbst.' *Ecology* **32:** 471–7.

J. Liebermann, 1960. 'Consideraciones sobre el control edafoecológico de tucuras (Orthoptera: Acridioidea) en la Argentina.' *Idia suppl. No.* **1:** 275–7.

F. Linke, 1943. 'Die Zahl der Sättigungstunden, ein neues bioklimatisches Element.' *Biokli. Beibl.* **10:** 70–3.

D. B. Long, 1953. 'Effects of population density on larvae of Lepidoptera.' *Trans. R. ent. Soc. Lond.* **104:** 541–91.

O.A.Lorenz, 1950. 'Air and soil temperatures in potato fields . . . during spring and early summer.' *Amer. Potato J.* **27**: 396–407.

T.T.Macan, 1962. 'Ecology of aquatic insects.' *Ann. Rev. Ent.* **7**: 261–88.

D.S.Maclagen and E.Dunn, 1956. 'The experimental analysis of the growth of an insect population.' *Proc. Roy. Soc.* **155**: 126–39.

K. Mazek Fialla, 1941. 'Die Körpertemperatur poikilothermer Thiere im Abhangigkeit vom Kleinklima.' *Z. wiss. Zool.* **154**: 170–247.

A.N.Mel'Nichenko, 1949. *Forest shelter-belts of the Trans-Volga steppes and their effects on the multiplication of animals useful and harmful to agriculture.* Moscow [in Russian].

M.Mikolajski, 1961. 'Quantitative relation of *Lygus pratensis* (L.) and *Lygus rugulipennis* Popp. (Heteroptera: Miridae) in clover and alfalfa plantings in the Provinces of Olsztyn., *Zeszyt., nauk. Wyźsz. Szk. roln. Olsztynie* **11** *No.* 110: 151–61 [in Polish; summaries in Russian and English].

A.Milne, 1957. 'Theories of natural control of insect populations.' *Cold Spring Harbor Symposium on quantitative biology* **22**: 253–71.

A.Milne, 1957. 'The natural control of insect populations.' *Canad. Ent.* **89**: 193–213.

R.A.Morse, E.J.Dyce and A.C.Gould, 1965. 'The treatment of American foul brood in New York State.' *Bee World* **46**: 15–7.

H.Müller, 1953. 'Der Blattlaus Befallsflug in Bereich eines Ackerbohnen und eines Kartoffel bestandes.' *Beitr. ent.* **3**: 229–58.

R.Neuwith, 1953. 'Unterschiede im Luftaustausch eines Gipfel und einer Hochaltstation nachgewiesen durch Messungen der bodennaher Ozon.' *Met. Rdschau.* **6**: 201–4.

J.Neyman, T.Park and E.C.Scott, 1954–5. 'Struggle for existence. The *Tribolium* model: biological and statistical aspects.' *Proc. 3rd Berkeley. Symp. Math. Statist. Prov. Univ. California Press.* 41–79.

M.W.Nielson and W.E.Curries, 1962. 'Leafhoppers attacking alfalfa in the Salt River Valley of Arizona.' *J. anim. Ecol.* **55(5)**: 803–4.

M.I.Norris, 1954. 'Sexual maturation in the desert locust (*Schistocerca gregaria*) with special reference to the effects of grouping.' *Anti-Locust Bulletin* No. 18. 44 pp.

T.Park and M.Lloyd, 1955. 'Natural selection and the outcome of competition.' *Amer. Nat.* **89**: 235–40.

R.Pearl, 1932. 'The influence of density of population upon egg production in *Drosophila melanogaster*.' *J. exp. Zool.* **63**: 57–84.

R.L.Pienkowski and J.T.Medler, 1962. 'Effects of alfalfa cuttings on the

248

potato leaf-hopper *Empoasca fabae*.' *J. econ. Ent.* **55(6)**: 973–8.

R. Poisson and G. & G. Richard, 1957. 'Observations sur quelques essai-mages de Corises (insectes hétéroptères aquatiques) survenus en Bretagne au cours de l'été 1956.' *C.R. Acad. Sci.* Paris **244**: 1076–9.

A. A. Ponomareva, 1959. 'The pollination of alfalfa in western Kopet-Dal.' *Trudy Inst. Zool. Paras. Akad. Nauk. Turkmen. S.S.R.* **4**: 34–46 [in Russian].

S. Pradhan, 1957. 'The ecology of arid zone insects (excluding locusts and grasshoppers).' *Arid zone Res. UNESCO* **8**: 199–240.

F. N. Pravdin, 1957. 'Regularities in the formation of new complexes of injurious and useful insects following the introduction of Compositae in cultivation.' *Uchen. Zap. mosk. Pedag. Inst.* **100(5)**: 1–190 [in Russian].

H. Prilop, 1957. 'Untersuchungen über die Insektenfauna von Zücker-rübenfelder in der Umgebung Göttingen.' *Z. angew. Zool.* **44**: 447–507.

H. Rycroft, 1949. 'Random sampling of rainfall.' *J. S. Afr. Forest Ass.* **18**: 71–8.

G. Salt, 1953. 'The arthropod population of the soil in some East African pastures.' *Bull. ent. Res.* **43**: 203–20.

F. Schneider, 1962. 'Dispersal and migration.' *Ann. Rev. Ent.* **7**: 223–42 contains a most useful bibliography of 103 titles.

W. Schwenke, 1957. Über Biocönosentypen, Populationstypen, und Grado-cöntypen; ein Beitrag zur biocönologischen Fundierung der Massenwechsel-Erforschung der Insekten.' *Ber. Hundertj. dtsch. ent. Ges. Berlin* **1956**: 106–17.

R. F. Smith, 1959. 'Plant diseases, insects and weeds as affected by irrigation' Insects. *Proc. 1st Intersoc. Conf. Irrigation. San Francisco* **1957**: 71–6.

M. E. Solomon, 1957. 'Dynamics of insect populations.' *Ann. Rev. Ent.* **2**: 121–42.

T. R. E. Southwood, 1966. *Ecological Methods: with particular reference to the study of insect populations.* Methuen, London. 391 pp. (This recent textbook covers many of the topics discussed in the present volume, and has additional references.)

F. Takahashi, 1956. 'On the effect of population density on the power of reproduction of the almond moth *Ephestia cautella*.' *Res. Popul. Ecol. III Ent. Lab. Univ. Kyoto No.* **10**. 35 pp.

M. Thompson, 1924. 'The soil population. An investigation of the biology of the soil in certain districts of Aberystwyth.' *Ann. appl. Biol.* **11**: 349–94.

C. W. Thornthwaite and J. R. Mather, 'The role of evapotranspiration in climate.' *Arch. Meteor. Geoph. Bioklim.* **11**: 16–39.

H. H. Tippins, 1964. 'Effect of winter burning on some pests of alfalfa.' *J. econ. Ent.* **57(6)**: 1003–4.

W. Tischler, 1955. *Synökologie der Landtiere.* Berlin. 414 pp.

S. Tonzig, 1951. 'Osservationi supra le oscillazioni giornaliere della CO_2 dell'aria a disposizione delle piante superiori nei diverse periodi dell'anno.' *Nuovo Giorn. Bot. Ital. N.S.* **57**: 583–618.

R. Trappenberg, 1951. 'Untersuchungen über die mikroklimatischen Wirkungen künstliche Beregnung im Tabakbestand.' *Arch. Meteor Geoph. Bioklim* **3**: 149–67.

P. Trojan, 1958. 'The ecological niches of certain species of horse-flies (Diptera : Tabanidae) in the Kampinos Forest near Warsaw.' *Ekologia Polska A. vi. No.* **2**: 53–129.

G. C. Ullyett, 1953. 'Biomathematics and insect population problems: a critical review.' *Mem. ent. Soc. S. Afr. No.* **2**. 89 pp.

S. Utida, 1950. 'On the equilibrium state of the interacting population of an insect and its parasite.' *Ecology* **31**: 165–75.

B. P. Uvarov, 1961. 'Insect hazards in land development.' *SPAN*, London **4**: 154–7.

B. P. Uvarov, 1962. 'Development of arid lands and its ecological effects on their insect fauna.' *Arid Zone Res.* **18**: 235–48.

B. P. Uvarov, 1964. 'Problems of insect ecology in developing countries.' *J. appl. Ecol.* **1(1)**: 159–68.

P. E. Waggoner, and R. H. Shaw, 1950. 'An evaluation of dew point fluctuations in the microclimatic layer.' *Bull. Amer. Meteor. Soc.* **31**: 382–4.

H. R. Wallace, 1953. 'The ecology of the fauna of pine stumps.' *J. anim. Ecol.* **22**: 154–71.

K. E. F. Watt, 1962. 'Use of mathematics in population ecology.' *Ann. Rev. Ent.* **7**: 243–60.

K. E. F. Watt, 1955. 'Studies on population productivity. *I.* Three approaches to the optimum yield problem in populations of *Tribolium confusum*.' *Ecol. Monogr.* **25**: 269–99.

A. O. Weese, 1939. 'The effects of overgrazing on insect populations.' *Proc. Oklahoma Acad. Sci.* **19**: 95–9.

W. G. Wellington, 1949. 'Temperature measurements in ecological entomology.' *Nature* **163**: 614–5.

W. G. Wellington, 1957. 'The synoptic approach to studies of insects and climate.' *Ann. Rev. Ent.* **2**: 143–62.

R. H. Whittacker, 1952. 'A study of summer foliage insect communities in the Great Smoky Mountains.' *Ecol. Monogr.* **22**: 1–44.

250

H. Wierzejewski, 1950. 'Theoretisches und konstrucktives zur Messung der Abkühlungsgrösse.' *Arch. Meteor. Geoph. Bioklim.* **11**: 65–85.

C. B. Williams, 1945. 'Recent light trap catches of Lepidoptera in the United States analysed in relation to the logarithmic series and index of diversity.' *Ann. ent. Soc. Amer.* **38**: 357–64.

C. B. Williams, 1947. 'The generic relations of species in small ecological communities.' *J. anim. Ecol.* **16**: 11–8.

C. B. Williams, 1953. 'The relative abundance of different species in a wild animal population.' *J. anim. Ecol.* **22**: 14–31.

G. N. Wolcott, 1928. 'Increase of insect transmitted disease and insect damage through weed destruction in tropical agriculture.' *Ecology* **9**: 61–6.

E. K. Woodford(Ed.), 1963. *Crop production in a weed-free environment.* Oxford University Press. 114 pp.

Acknowledgments

Acknowledgment is due to the following for the illustrations (the number refers to the page on which the illustration appears). Frontispiece, 216 Harold Oldroyd; 10, 11, 80, 82, 96, 97, 99, 105, 107, 109, 120, 123, 129, 130, 206, 229, 238 Shell Photographic Service, London; 39, 52, 58, 59, 70 Rothamsted Experimental Station, Harpenden, England (photos L. R. Taylor); 149, 161 Plant Protection Limited, Imperial Chemical Industries, London; 230 The Farmers Weekly. The diagrams were drawn by Design Practitioners Limited.

Index

252

254

World University Library

Some books published or in preparation

Economics and Social Studies

The World Cities
Peter Hall, *London*

The Economics of Underdeveloped Countries
Jagdish Bhagwati, *Delhi*

Development Planning
Jan Tinbergen, *Rotterdam*

Decisive Forces in World Economics
J. L. Sampedro, *Madrid*

Key Issues in Criminology
Roger Hood, *Durham*

Human Communication
J. L. Aranguren, *Madrid*

Education in the Modern World
John Vaizey, *London*

History

The Emergence of Greek Democracy
W. G. Forrest, *Oxford*

Muhammad and the Conquests of Islam
Francesco Gabrieli, *Rome*

Humanism in the Renaissance
S. Dresden, *Leyden*

The Ottoman Empire
Halil Inalcik, *Ankara*

The Rise of Toleration
Henry Kamen, *Warwick*

The Left in Europe
David Caute, *Oxford*

The Rise of the Working Class
Jürgen Kuczynski, *Berlin*

Chinese Communism
Robert C. North, *Stanford*

Philosophy and Religion

Christianity
W. O. Chadwick, *Cambridge*

Monasticism
David Knowles, *London*

Judaism
J. Soetendorp, *Amsterdam*

The Modern Papacy
K. O. von Aretin, *Gottingen*

Sects
Bryan Wilson, *Oxford*

Language and Literature

A Model of Language
E. M. Uhlenbeck, *Leyden*

French Literature
Raymond Picard, *Paris*

Russian Writers and Society
Ronald Hingley, *Oxford*

Satire
Matthew Hodgart, *Sussex*

The Arts

Primitive Art
Eike Haberland, *Mainz*

The Language of Modern Art
Ulf Linde, *Stockholm*

Aesthetic Theories since 1850
J. F. Revel, *Paris*

Art Nouveau
S. T. Madsen, *Oslo*

Academic Painting
Gerald Ackerman, *Stanford*

Palaeolithic Cave Art
P. J. Ucko and A. Rosenfeld, *London*

Psychology and Human Biology

Eye and Brain
R. L. Gregory, *Cambridge*

The Ear and the Brain
Edward Carterette, *U.C.L.A.*

The Variety of Man
J. P. Garlick, *London*

The Biology of Work
O. G. Edholm, *London*

Psychoses
H. J. Bochnik, *Hamburg*

Child Development
Philippe Muller, *Neuchâtel*

Man and Disease
Gernot Rath, *Göttingen*

Chinese Medicine
P. Huard and M. Wong, *Paris*

The Psychology of Fear and Stress
J. A. Gray, *Oxford*

Zoology and Botany

Animal Communication
J. M. Cullen, *Oxford*

Mimicry
Wolfgang Wickler, *Seewiesen*

Migration
Gustaf Rudebeck, *Stockholm*

The World of an Insect
Rémy Chauvin, *Strasbourg*

Biological Rhythms
Janet Harker, *Cambridge*

Lower Animals
Martin Wells, *Cambridge*

Dinosaurs
Bjöon Kurtén, *Helsinki*

3604

Physical Science and Mathematics

Mathematics Observed
H. Freudenthal, *Utrecht*

The Quest for Absolute Zero
K. Mendelssohn, *Oxford*

Particles and Accelerators
Robert Gouiran, *C.E.R.N., Geneva*

Optics
A. C. S. van Heel and
C. H. F. Velzel, *Eindhoven*

Waves and Corpuscles
J. L. Andrade e Silva and
G. Lochak, *Paris*
Introduction by Louis de Broglie

Energy
J. Fischhoff, *Paris*

Earth Sciences and Astronomy

The Electrical Earth
J. Sayers, *Birmingham*

Climate and Weather
H. Flohn, *Bonn*

The Structure of the Universe
E. L. Schatzman, *Paris*

Applied Science

Words and Waves
A. H. W. Beck, *Cambridge*

The Science of Decision-Making
A. Kaufmann, *Paris*

Bioengineering
H. S. Wolff, *London*

Bionics
Lucien Gerardin, *Paris*

Metals and Civilisation
R. W. Cahn, *Sussex*